A LITTLE BOOK OF IMPRESSIONS

A LIFE IN THE DAY OF A DENTIST

Gerald Feaver

Matador
Unit E2 Airfield Business Park,
Harrison Road, Market Harborough,
Leicestershire. LE16 7UL
Tel: 0116 2792299
Email: books@troubador.co.uk
Web: www.troubador.co.uk/matador
Twitter: @matadorbooks

ISBN 978 1803130 217

British Library Cataloguing in Publication Data.
A catalogue record for this book is available from the British Library.

Printed and bound in Great Britain by 4edge Limited
Typeset in 11pt Adobe Caslon Pro by Troubador Publishing Ltd, Leicester, UK

Matador is an imprint of Troubador Publishing Ltd

To Judy
For her love and unwavering support.

A LITTLE BOOK OF IMPRESSIONS

Revealing lives behind the mirror and probe.

CONTENTS

FOREWORD

For sixty years I lived in abject fear of dentists. My first introduction to one, as a small boy growing up in Brighton, did not go well. Leonard Morey, who may to the outside world have been charm personified, was, to the four-year-old me, Laurence Olivier in *Marathon Man* on steroids.

He stooped; he wore some kind of white, blood-spattered sterile cloak; he had hypodermic syringes the size of fire extinguishers; he had a nurse who smiled like Rosa Klebb in From *Russia With Love*. But worst of all, horror of all horrors, he had a drill that he pedalled by foot. I still wake some nights and hear those sounds: the pedalling, the grinding, the whine of the bit grinding my teeth and the agonising pain it inflicted.

Mr Morey's drill was replaced with an electric one, and then when I was older, I replaced Mr Morey with a dentist first in Canada where I had moved to, then back in Sussex, all the time each visit preceded by a deep, dark dread. Especially my last Sussex dentist who told me he took a Valium tablet before doing any drilling because it upset him to inflict pain!

And then one day, now living in London, I had lunch with a man whose brains I was picking for a new novel, and he told me about a quite remarkable and utterly charming dentist, called Gerald Feaver, in Harley Street. Tony Balazs, my friend, said that through visiting Feaver, he had completely lost his fear of dentists.

Although I didn't entirely believe him, I decided to give Gerald Feaver a go. After all, he couldn't be worse than any of my previous dentists. But on entering the Feaver surgery, I froze. There in front of the window was a foot-pedalled drill, just like the one of my old childhood nemesis!

But there was something about Gerald's calm nature that instantly put me at ease, in a way no previous dentist ever had. Afterwards I told my wife, Lara, who also lived in some terror of dentists. She made an appointment with him and came home all smiles. Gerald had worked his magic spell on us. His humour, his charm and his consummate skill. I don't remember one instant of pain during all the time I was lucky enough to have him as my dentist and it was the same for Lara.

From that point onwards both of us actually looked forward to going to see him – something I had never believed would be possible. It was a sad day for us both when he retired. So, it's a true joy to have these memoirs to read and look back on. And I can think of no better place to do this than reclining in a dentist's chair!

Peter James
2021

INTRODUCTION

Having been a dentist for over forty years, my life has been enriched by the amazing people I have met working as a dentist and hearing their remarkable stories (yes, we do allow our patients to speak sometimes!). I do like chatting. It has helped over the years to relax patients so they don't feel rushed. It helps build a relationship which hopefully will last for many years. For me, it added another dimension to the work which I did and loved. Now that I am retired, I wanted to share some of my experiences.

Many medical memoirs have been written, stories detailing the work of doctors in their many roles, performing life-saving procedures and often in dangerous conditions. Others have focused on the lives of doctors in unusual circumstances, either in a war-torn country or closer to home, in prisons where drug use and mental illness are rife. Some have looked at the daily routine in hospitals, the workload and stress induced in those who struggle to help others survive. Humour, often black humour, is never far away, helping as it does to sustain those working often against the odds and reducing the pressure in the tense situations that arise when delivering care in our hospitals.

Other books, like the *Doctor in the House* series written by Richard Gordon (himself a doctor) in the 1950s, painted brilliant caricatures of doctors and hospital life and were full of humorous exploits.

Reading many years ago *It Shouldn't Happen to a Vet*, it occurred to me that perhaps it shouldn't happen to a dentist either, but it did. It was then that the seeds were sown. I wanted to write a light-hearted resume of life in dental practice, what led me there and the experiences and encounters I had along the way.

I felt privileged to share these stories, many of which would never be retold and would be forgotten forever. I hoped that writing this would provide a glimpse – sometimes humorous, sometimes poignant – behind the mirror, probe and drill. I wanted to reveal the human side of dentistry, the care and compassion that we strive to achieve when treating our patients and so help in some small way to reduce the fear that many still have about a visit to the dentist's chair.

'People don't care how much you know until they know how much you care'.

Theodore Roosevelt

ONE

CUTTING TEETH

She lay back, her long red hair flowing over her shoulders. Her weathered, worn features belied her age, her youthful eyes reflecting previous unspoken images like a photo book of past experiences.

Her lips parted, her eyes closed, wincing in anticipation. Briefly, impatiently, they flickered. "Is this your first time?" she muttered. "Just be gentle; that's all I ask."

Slowly, trembling and trying to hide my nervousness, I gently inserted the needle into the soft tissues around her decayed upper molar. "There," she said, "that wasn't so bad."

And so began my long career in dentistry.

In truth, I believe the seeds were sown, literally unknowingly, many years before. But first to my background and the path that led me to become a dentist.

I was born in Folkestone just after the Second World War, the youngest of three children living in Cheriton at the foot of the South Downs surrounded by countryside, a far cry from the hustle and bustle of the Eurotunnel Terminus that it is today.

After a few years at Harcourt House Primary School, where my abiding memories are of my pet tortoise peeing on me in front of the class on a 'show your pet day' and, as an eight-year-old, having my first crush. Cheryl Reeves, exotic-looking with her olive skin, dark hair and bright smile, was considerably older than me and rejected my advances out of hand in spite of me presenting her with a half-eaten box of chocolates.

I graduated to Westbrook House, a prep school, just before my ninth birthday. I loved that school, friends and teachers, disciplined but never harshly so. A headmaster by the name of Ken Foster instilled respect, showed compassion and taught us the important values in life. I was not a sportsman but even I managed to excel at fencing under the tutorship of our PE master Professor Mallard, an ex-marine Sergeant Major who wore his professorship like a badge of honour. He took no prisoners and employed the same military discipline on us as he must have displayed on the battlefield to his troops.

Saturday afternoons were the highlight of the week. After an hour or so of sport, outdoors whatever the weather, we would crowd into the wooden assembly hall sustained by mugs of hot cocoa and bread and dripping to be treated to a film.

The headmaster would show black and white movies such as Norman Wisdom comedies, westerns and war films, and for me, the most memorable, *Doctor in the House*. In the winter months, after the film we would crowd around the headmaster at the far end of the hall to watch as he started up his model railway, an intricate network of bridges, tunnels and viaducts as the trains criss-crossed the imaginary countryside and we escaped to another world. In the summer months, he would start up not his railway but his sit-upon motor mower and set off to cut the grass on the extensive sports fields, followed by a procession of schoolboys, like groupies to a much-admired celebrity.

I learnt to swim at Westbrook House. Although I was born near the sea, swimming didn't come naturally to me. Every week, come rain or shine (except presumably in the winter months), we were taken to an outdoor pool by the sea. The chalk blackboard gave the day's water temperature and rarely did it reach 68°F (20°C). My swimming teacher was Sam Rockett, who had swum the channel. I am sure his aim was to make all of us into potential channel swimmers. With me, he failed miserably. I did eventually manage to be awarded my blue ribbon, signifying I could swim one width of the pool, and then only because I managed to keep one foot on the bottom of the pool without him noticing.

It was many years later that I overcame my fear of being out of my depth, by which time I had children of my own who took to the water more readily than I did.

Alcohol had never passed my lips at Westbrook House, until, that is, when I was around twelve and I was invited to a friend's for Sunday lunch. His father was a rector in rural Kent and before sitting down to eat, I was given a glass of sherry. Too embarrassed to refuse, I drank it. The rest of the day passed off in a haze, with the walls of the ancient vicarage spinning around me.

At the other extreme was our mildly or wildly eccentric Latin teacher. Delivering his classes with a forced speech impediment which exaggerated the Latin tenses as if they were spoken by a Roman centurion in a wind tunnel, he had a peculiar way of ensuring we learnt our grammar.

Any misdemeanour, or forgetfulness, or error on our part, we would be summoned to the front of the class where, grunting, he would pull our heads down onto his lap and recite loudly: "Amo, amas, amat!" whilst at the same time drumming our heads with a closed fist. We would never have considered this inappropriate, but in the 21st century the consequences and conclusions could be entirely different.

I was by no means musical. In fact, I had the dubious honour of being the only one in my class not to pass the audition for the school choir. I had only sung two lines of 'Onward Christian Soldiers' when our music teacher, Mrs Thirlow, stopped playing the piano and told me not to bother. I hadn't seen her cry before.

We didn't regard our teachers as ogres, and we looked up to them. Some were more predictable than others.

Mr Metcalfe, our Geography teacher, regaled us with stories of his wartime exploits in a destroyer. Whenever he showed us a map of the world, he would proudly announce that the red areas depicting the British Commonwealth were ours. "They belong to you and me," he would say. It was as if the war wasn't over for him, and he was still conquering the world.

4

I was reminded of his naval adventures many many years afterwards when I treated a real hero of the Second World War, but more of that later.

We had the good fortune to be taught English by Humphrey Household. His brother, Geoffrey Household, was a prolific writer of novels and children's books, including the acclaimed thriller *Rogue Male*, and was literally a household name at the time. I sometimes wonder whether at such an early age we ever recognised literary talent.

Envy is not attractive, and I have never been an envious person. Except when it came to Mr Blee, one of the younger teachers. He taught us History with the enthusiasm and vigour that I am sure he also adopted in his private life. And the cause of us schoolboys' envy was that he fell in love with and married the school matron. She was young and attractive, and illness at school shot up with queues every lunchtime outside Matron's room.

She was in sharp contrast to the previous matron in her starched uniform with a personality to match. We dreaded the prospect of not feeling well. On one occasion when I went to see her with stomach pain, she told me to sit on the loo and not get up until I had performed. She then came to inspect what looked more like the deposit of my pet rabbit. She was satisfied and I could go. Unfortunately for me, I still had stomach ache.

Next door to my school was the dentist I had been going to all my childhood.

Sidney Smith was an eccentric, and to a young child, elderly, silver-haired, kind and softly spoken man, whose surgery – with its floor-to-ceiling window – overlooked the main London to Dover railway line. Just as well, as he loved trains, leaping up to point out the *Golden Arrow*, a majestic steam train, as it thundered past. He always ran late, probably because he talked so much, usually to my mother, whom he seemed to take a shine to. Most dentists in those days would have an array of *Punch* magazines and goldfish in the waiting room. Sidney Smith had a monkey!

I was an anxious patient, suspicious of all the paraphernalia of his profession. One day, knowing how nervous I was about having a tooth out, he suggested hypnotising me. It worked like a dream. I can remember him vividly placing an instrument over my head and asking me to stare at it and beginning to feel drowsy. His quiet, gentle voice told me that, firstly, my arm would become so heavy I would be unable to lift it – which I couldn't – and then, that my tooth would become heavy and numb, at which point it must have been dispatched. The only surprise came later that day when on my way to bed. I always kissed my mother goodnight, but on this occasion, I kissed her twice "Why did you kiss me twice?" my mother asked.

"Oh," I said, "one was for me and one was from Sidney." Obviously, post-hypnotic suggestion worked, although what words he actually uttered to me I have no idea.

Some years later, about to sit my common entrance examination, Sidney knew from my parents that I was anxious and worried. He told me to see him the day before. He sat me down and I can hear his calming voice now, telling me I would have no worries and no anxieties and would remember all I needed to. I passed – another successful post-hypnotic suggestion.

Maybe he saw in me the potential to be a dentist and sowed the seeds all those years ago. But then something else happened that may have had some further influence on the direction I would take.

Life was about to change. Having been cocooned in the comfort of Westbrook House, I found myself at Dover College – often described as a minor public school on the south coast – initially as a day boy, travelling by steam train from Folkestone. To us as schoolboys, this was an experience we took for granted, the monotony only broken by the excitement of travelling on the first electric train.

Dover was a bustling harbour town but archaic in many ways. No dials on the telephones, you just lifted the receiver and waited an interminable time for the operator to ask, "Number, please." Not that we were meant to make telephone calls. After my first year, my father – who worked for an insurance company – was relocated to Chelmsford, and I became a border. The transition was not an easy one. Sleeping in a dormitory, strict rules and not allowed to leave the school grounds except at designated times, the regime seemed harsh. Fagging (where younger pupils had to carry out menial tasks for senior boys) and initiations still happened, but it was their twilight days. Boys could be cruel but not in subtle ways. I remember one boy who had such enormous testicles, the reason for his nickname 'Balls' was obvious to everyone.

I soon adjusted to and enjoyed life there. But there were disappointments. I joined the sea scouts to find they were devoid of boats so most of us had to walk or be driven to camps rather than go by sea. I also joined the sailing club and ended up rowing the senior boys out to the yachts and rarely sailing myself. My housemaster was Edward Bailey, tall and imposing and totally bald; he taught Latin and spoke with a mild grunt (maybe this is a prerequisite of all Latin teachers). His wife ran the house and clearly had her favourites but was sympathetic and maternal, if somewhat intimidating, probably in part due to her dog, a chow chow which always had a menacing look when any boy approached her.

Unless you were excused on the grounds of religion, joining the CCF (army cadets) was compulsory. I was a signaller. We had three walkie-talkies left over from the war: one could send messages, one could receive, and one could do both. Not a lot of use when you were lost on exercises but helpful if you wanted to escape detection in the pub.

We were equipped with Lee Enfield First World War rifles and blank ammunition. Whether it was wise to let fifteen-year-old boys march through the streets of Dover heavily armed was never questioned. Discipline was maintained by the masters, who somehow seemed to have an alter ego as commissioned officers in HM Forces. To see the biology master calling parade to order seemed a little incongruous.

I learnt to drive at Dover College or, more accurately, I was taught how one should drive.

My driving instructor towered over me at six foot ten. Such was his stature that I recall sitting in his dual controlled Ford Anglia with him sitting on the rear seat, having removed the front passenger seat to give him more leg room.

There was a strong sporting ethos at Dover College, which may be one reason why my father chose the school. If so, he was sadly misguided. Sport flowed in my father's veins but not in mine. In the Territorial Army before the Second World War, he was literally called up at the outbreak of war from the cricket field in Folkestone, where he captained the local team.

Growing up, I heard little of my father's war exploits, but two episodes that he recounted to me stick in my mind. Stationed initially in Dover in 1939, eventually attaining the rank of Major in the Royal Artillery, he requisitioned an army lorry to collect essential supplies for his gunners. These took the form of much-needed beer from the local Mackeson Brewery where my father knew the Brewery manager from before the war. I am sure that this raised the spirits of his men. Later in the war, in Suffolk, he gave orders for the shooting down of an enemy bomber. Unfortunately, the aircraft was American, but luckily the crew all bailed out with only the pilot sustaining a broken leg. It crashed on the railway line in Darsham where the bombs exploded. The *East Anglian Daily Times* reported a woodman being blown from his bicycle in the ensuing explosions. He turned out to be the father of the secretary who was to work for my father after the war when he was demobbed and returned to the Royal Insurance Company in Folkestone. Another coincidence came some thirty years later.

In 1970, my parents retired to Suffolk and were living near Darsham. Visiting the pub at the railway station, my father was intrigued to hear the discussion centring on the crashing of the American bomber all those years before. On enquiring, he was told the pilot of the doomed aircraft had been in the pub the week before. My father kept quiet.

Apart from cricket, my father also played rugby. He played for his county and captained the Dover team. Locally, his name was well known, which gave me a certain kudos. I possessed none of my father's sporting prowess, which may go some way to explain what happened in the gym. Our PE master was Jeffrey Archer, former politician and well-known novelist. We had been told that an Oxford athlete was coming to teach at Dover College for a year. We were somewhat in awe; tough, enthusiastic, determined with a hint of ruthlessness, Jeffrey Archer recognised sporting ability in his pupils. For one who possessed little sporting ability, PE lessons could be a struggle. Practising for a school PE display, I was climbing onto a fellow pupil's shoulders when I lost my balance, landed heavily and hit my face, an upper front tooth scurrying across the wooden floor. "What are you doing down there, boy? Get up on those shoulders." Harsh, yes, but in retrospect probably the best way of dealing with it. Being comforted and cuddled was no way to make a man. So, I went back to Sidney Smith.

I didn't excel academically at school. I enjoyed biology, taught by a master known as 'Ratty' because of his resemblance to the animals he was dissecting. Physics was somewhat of a mystery. The teacher, a gentle soul whose surname Sankey unfortunately rhymed with a word often associated with schoolboy humour. And that became the name we knew him by. His lessons were frequently disrupted by one particularly unruly pupil who variously discharged fire extinguishers, let off stink bombs and passed around copies of *Health and Efficiency* magazine, which was the closest any of us got to pornography.

Our teachers included a delightful Mr Robinson from Northallerton, who drove around in a bright blue Renault Dauphine and spoke in such a strong Yorkshire accent when delivering his Geography lessons that many of us southerners needed an interpreter, and an elderly History master who seemed as ancient as the subject he was teaching.

Maths was my toughest subject, taught by a Maths master who, for some obscure reason, was called the Aunt. I passed my O-level at the fourth attempt. The headmaster, Timothy Cobb, was a charismatic figure. His gently authoritative personality commanded respect.

School prefects, distinguished by their black boaters and the permission to put hands in their pockets, were appointed on merit, usually on sporting achievement. So, when I was appointed, it came as a shock. School prefects could dispense punishments, but I was a soft touch. Certainly, I would never have caned anyone, and even lesser punishments, such as writing out the school rules ten times for talking after lights out, seemed a step too far. My appointment as a school prefect may have been due to the perceived contribution I made to the community. Looking back, I wonder how this came about, but again this might have had some bearing on the direction I was to take.

By volunteering to help in the local community, I got involved with visiting an elderly man who I am sure appreciated my company but for the most part sat glued to his black and white television, watching motor racing with exclamations about Stirling Moss and Mike Hawthorn.

But my visits to the local psychiatric hospital through the same school-sponsored community scheme were most memorable. Stark and depressing, I was assigned washing-up duties. Vivid memories of piles of pans and dirty washing-up water, acrid smells and a humourless environment. Whether those I worked with were staff or inmates, for that's what they were called, was difficult to determine. But this experience opened my eyes. In my previous sheltered existence, I would not have encountered people in need of compassion and help.

I grew up in a loving environment and my mother demonstrated what compassion meant.

She was born into a working-class family, one of five siblings. A sister died young from the scourge of tuberculosis, and a brother was lost at sea in the war.

My mother always wanted to be a doctor, but her lowly and somewhat impoverished background did not permit it. She went to London in the early 1930s and trained to be a nurse at the Whittington Hospital, where she excelled in her year. She married my father in the August of 1936. They had grown up together in Wouldham, a village on the shores of the River Medway in Kent. My mother was the daughter of an electrician at the local cement works and her mother, known as Rooney, was a diminutive four foot ten chain smoker who delighted in hiding from her grandchildren in kitchen cupboards. By the age of eleven, I was taller than her.

By contrast, my father's parents were Victorian in their behaviour, outlook and attitude. My grandfather ran a successful butcher's shop and was a shrewd investor. Although my father never discussed money, I learnt later that he never had a mortgage, their first home purchased for them by his father. I remember that as a child in the 1950s, our first television set was a gift from my grandfather.

My mother continued nursing and during the war, when my father was called up, looked after children as Matron at a nursery in St Neots, by which time she had two children, Alan and Carol, who stayed with her.

She continued nursing into her fifties, although many would say well beyond that as, even after she had reached her centenary, she could be seen dispensing care and the occasional paracetamol to the younger residents of the care home she moved into. "I'm a qualified nurse," she would proudly announce when another resident fell ill.

I like to think that the love and compassion she showed me was a guiding force in my life.

Growing up, I was never close to my brother. He was ten years older than me and led his own life. My sister Carol and I, however, in spite of the age gap, were always close. Carol was eight years older but was always looking out for me, although not always successfully.

We lived in Folkestone and when I was four years old, we went on a family holiday to Broadstairs just a few miles along the south coast. There were five of us plus a dog, which must have been a tight squeeze piled into my father's Morris Minor. I loved buses and I pleaded with my parents to let me and my sister travel by bus to Broadstairs, where we would be met at the other end by my parents. What I remember of that journey is getting hopelessly lost with Carol in tears, as we had got off at the wrong stop in totally the wrong place. When we eventually arrived, both my parents were at the police station and loudspeaker appeals were being broadcast on the streets of Broadstairs.

I always enjoyed spending time with my sister. A more

successful trip was to visit her in London where she was training to be a nurse. For me, as a twelve-year-old schoolboy, this was a great adventure and gave me a taste for London which I have grown to love.

I have always seen the funny side of life, and this was nurtured and fuelled by those trips to stay with my sister. She would take me to the Whitehall Theatre to see the Brian Rix farces. Although I perhaps didn't always appreciate the double entendres of farces, seeing grown men losing their trousers and hiding in cupboards, disappearing and reappearing behind closed doors, was, to me, side-splittingly funny.

I firmly believe that this humour has helped me through life and, I hope, has been evident in the way I have practised dentistry over the years. Serious moments, of course, and for so many, a visit to the dentist is an ordeal. I wanted my patients to enjoy rather than endure treatment. Not that that ever entered my head when I was a child.

Back at Dover College there was little career guidance. The careers room consisted of a table containing a range of pamphlets on what was available; for many of us, university was not an automatic choice.

I left Dover College with two A-levels under my belt but no idea where I would be heading next.

TWO

THE OUTSIDE WORLD

I left school in 1967 and explored various career options. I was accepted onto a hospital management training course which combined study for a diploma in hospital management with my first job as a hospital management trainee.

I was assigned to The London Hospital in Whitechapel in the heart of London's East End where the notorious Kray twins ruled the criminal underworld. The Blind Beggar pub where an underworld killing had taken place at that time was a few hundred yards away. For me, this was an alien world.

My first job was as a medical records clerk in the bowels of the earth beneath the hospital where I joined an army of East End women filing and retrieving notes, swearing, gossiping and smoking incessantly. I was the only male.

What they made of me, a public schoolboy, plunged into this other world, I have no idea. But if there was any animosity, they never showed it. They took me under their wing and included me in everything. They tried to fix me up on dates. One girl in particular befriended me. We laughed and joked, and I could have fallen for her. I was crestfallen when she became pregnant and left.

Promotion followed as a clerk in the admissions office, run by two East End characters, Gordon Hutcheon and Bill Wogan. They ran a tight ship with typical East End humour. Standing in front of a huge board depicting bed availability, theirs was a daily battle with the consultants and ward sisters who needed to find beds. It reminded me of the aircraft plotting charts of the Second World War, and they were always one step ahead. On the board, the current bed status would be shown. Consultants would waltz in with their juniors, peruse their waiting lists and determine who would be summoned to hospital. The admissions officers had to find the beds. They rarely failed. One of the more flamboyant consultants, often dressed in pink attire, would many years later become a patient of mine.

Bill Wogan drove a Messerschmidt bubble car. He nearly didn't make it in one day. These cars had no reverse gear, with a door opening at the front of the vehicle. He unfortunately parked it face on to a brick wall, couldn't open the door and couldn't reverse. Only his continued hooting alerted passers-by to his dilemma.

The hospital was very hierarchical. At the top was the House Governor, with his minions beneath him who managed the hospital. It was a fine balancing act to ensure the hospital ran smoothly and the will of the all-important consultants was not frustrated and at the same time the interests of Matron and her sisters were not sidelined. And then, of course, there were the patients.

For many, the consultants were revered and treated like gods. But the nurses were delightful and dedicated and I got drawn into their world and even into their rooms. It was a welcome relief for my next role which, ironically, also came under the auspices of the admissions office. This was dealing with the demise of those patients who didn't make it. For a nineteen-year-old, this was the most depressing job imaginable. Handing over the death certificate and poignant personal effects to weeping relatives in a dingy, dark partitioned room made a profound impression on me. It was the only time I have ever been unhappy in my work. Black humour stalked the corridors of the hospital, and there were moments of light relief.

The House Governor's elderly father was admitted to hospital. He was being wheeled along the corridor on the way to his ward on the first floor. The lift was out of order. "No problem," said the aged patient, "I can climb the stairs."

"What about the wheelchair?" asked the porter.

"I'll help you carry it," replied the patient. And together, they did. The House Governor didn't see the funny side.

My next posting was the catalyst that would change my life.

Part of The London Hospital was the Dental Institute. It was a dental school for training aspiring dentists and offered treatment to the local population. There was no shortage of patients queuing up and filling the waiting rooms for free treatment.

My job was to assist Joan Ashmore, the Head Administrator, in the running of the Dental Hospital. Quietly efficient, she would direct me in my mundane tasks. I met dental students my own age carrying out a variety of treatments that to me, on the fringes of their world, was fascinating. I guess I was envious of their situation. Whilst I was pen-pushing, they were wielding mirrors, probes, dental drills and forceps, but more than this, there was a camaraderie that I had never experienced. And at the end of their day, they must have felt some pride in what they had achieved, whilst I trudged my way home, secure in the knowledge my only achievement was that I had prepared all the files for the next day's patients. And there was a certain kudos in what they did and respect for the consultants who taught them.

I may have aspired to what they did, but their world seemed beyond my grasp. With insufficient A-levels even to get to university and no sciences beyond O-level, it seemed studying dentistry was a forlorn hope.

I was not going to give up.

I took a further A-level, not a science, as that would have been a step too far, but in Politics, as that was covered in my hospital management course. I wrote a letter to Guy's Hospital, one of the oldest teaching hospitals in London, where the Medical and Dental Schools were offering an extended course for students with Arts A-levels. They invited me to apply through UCAS, which was then in its infancy, and my application passed the first hurdle.

My interview at Guy's was in the Medical School, a separate imposing building over a hundred years old, with ivy-clad walls overlooking a close where students and nurses were gathered, lying in the sun during their lunch breaks. I entered into a dark, somewhat foreboding, hallway where I was directed into an expansive meeting room and seated at a large, oval table opposite four inscrutable seated men. They must have introduced themselves, but such was my anxiety I cannot remember their names nor much of what I was asked. That day remains a haze, but I must have passed the test as a letter arrived offering me a place to study Dentistry in October that year.

I couldn't contain my excitement. I handed in my notice at The London Hospital with, I have to say, a degree of sadness and left with offers to employ me during the long vacations. In retrospect, that was a rash offer, but more of that later.

I had found accommodation in a student hall in Ealing at the very opposite end of the Central Line from Guy's Hospital. Situated in the leafy suburb of Ealing, The Moulin Hostel was home to students at various colleges from across London. The name conjures up the more famous venue in Paris and there was, coincidentally, a connection with music and dance, although of an entirely different variety. Amongst the fifty or so students, there was a sizeable contingent from the Royal Ballet School who introduced an element of glamour into our student lives.

London then, like now, was a dynamic city, and I fell in love with its vibrancy, culture and history. So much to see and do, but I managed on a limited budget.

The Hall was run by a Miss Doris Jones from Dolgellau under the auspices of the Methodist Church; there was a strict no alcohol and even stricter no sex policy. But then, rules are there to be broken! Miss Jones, an outwardly fierce Welsh Dragon, had a soft, kind heart beneath her fiery exterior. On one occasion when water was gushing out the overflow pipe from the men's floor, she had no qualms about entering the bathroom (there were no locks), calling out, "I'm coming in," and pulling the plug out whilst the hapless occupant just lay there.

I arrived at Guy's for my first day with a mixture of apprehension, enthusiasm and excitement. Dating back to the 18th century and a few hundred yards from London Bridge in the heart of Southwark, the hospital entrance was through a great colonnade, opening out onto the campus opposite the Medical School.

I was one of the more mature students (in years at any rate), unlike most who had come straight from school. There were, however, about a dozen of us who had previously worked or studied elsewhere. Thrown together, we soon formed a cohesive group. We were the ones embarking on an extra foundation year, some of whom would go on to study medicine and some dentistry. Our backgrounds were diverse. There was a Norwegian contingent, including an ex-soldier, but most were from the UK. I can recall my first lecture and the hard, wooden bench seats of the lecture theatre and wondering what illustrious forebears had sat there before me.

I immersed myself into life as a student. Our days were filled with lectures and, slowly, the mystery of the sciences unravelled, although somewhat like the plot of a complicated detective story, some aspects had twists and turns that were seemingly incomprehensible.

By today's standards, the lectures were formal and the lecturers more so, and you rarely missed a lecture. We were addressed by our surnames, but the quality of the teaching was in no doubt. The subjects – Biology, Chemistry and Physics – were taught with the focus on their application to medicine and dentistry.

Physics, however, remained a mystery. For most of us, this was our first exposure to serious physics, and the tone of the lectures was always serious. Complex graphs, theories, radiation doses, refraction, reflection, but there was no Eureka moment for me. Taught by Dr Wyard, an eminent physicist himself, he had outgrown the level of student humour that many of us possessed. There were nonetheless some interludes of light relief, mainly during the practical experiments when they went disastrously wrong.

I did learn, however, that although the theory was hard to grasp, the practical application of these theories was what mattered, and that became clear to me throughout my studies and beyond.

The first occasion that I wielded a scalpel was in the biology classes, either to dissect a dogfish, frog or mouse, but even then, I suspect some fellow students imagined they were performing some life-saving operation.

I was acutely aware of the pressure to pass my first year's exams – failure to do so would result in a resit at best or expulsion at worse. I had extra tuition during the vacations with one of the biology teachers, a tall, lanky but infinitely patient man, Dr Bannister, who taught me much.

Chemistry was taught as two distinct subjects: physical chemistry and organic chemistry. The physical chemistry lecturer intrigued me, not so much the subject, which I could just about grasp, but the question that was occupying most of our minds as we grappled with complex formulae: why did he wear such an ill-fitting and obvious wig?

Organic chemistry seemed unfathomable. I can't blame the lecturer, a laid-back Dr Gent; in fact, I have much to thank him for, as the upcoming exams would prove. The end-of-year exams were rapidly approaching. Partying stopped, or slowed down, and the serious study began.

Exams were both written and practical with a dreaded viva (oral exam) if you were borderline.

I remember lunchtime on the day the results were due. We were in the Spit, the appropriately named dining area where we ate every day. Suddenly the word was out; the results had been announced. Although I had passed Biology and Physics, Chemistry was borderline. My mark in physical Chemistry was high, but I had only scored a paltry fifteen per cent in organic Chemistry. I was to be given a viva that afternoon. And this is where the camaraderie kicked in. 'Just revise one topic now, and we will test you' was the advice from my peers, who had all sailed through. So, I did, and they tested me over lunch. Fortunately, the examiner was Dr Gent, who had lectured us throughout. "Is there nothing you understand about organic Chemistry?" he asked.

"I do understand some of it," I said.

Somewhat disbelievingly, "Tell me what," he said.

"Alcohol," I suggested. And so, I proceeded to tell him all about the chemistry of alcohol, none of which I had known that morning and most of which I would not remember, but I passed. Alcohol saved the day, and much was consumed that night as we celebrated our success. The term ended and a long vacation awaited.

Needing to earn money to supplement my grant, I returned to The London Hospital where I was told I would always be welcome.

I was assigned to the Works Department under the direction of Mr Froom, a kind man who always took his responsibilities seriously and often wore a worried expression on his face. Situated in the basement this was a hub of activity crucial in ensuring the hospital ran smoothly and all the stock was regularly replenished.

I was given a desk in an office shared with Helen, a chatty secretary, and Cyril, the Head of Central Sterilisation, a camp, charming man who was the essence of politeness even when things were going wrong. And there were a few disasters.

I guess my nature is to try and help, and perhaps in this I can be too enthusiastic, for example giving up my seat to a man carrying a white stick, only to discover that he was not blind but merely carrying a curtain rail. But I digress.

Sitting opposite the efficient Helen, typing away, I noticed a large wasp had landed on her leg. "Stay still," I shouted and swatted the offending insect with my rolled-up newspaper. The sting caused her leg to swell to twice its size. She was off work for a week.

Mr Froom went on his vacation and left me to oversee ordering central supplies. In those days, clinical waste was disposed of in bitumen-lined sacks. Instead of ordering five thousand, somehow, I had added an extra nought and fifty thousand were delivered. The storeroom was overflowing, the corridors stacked high with these sacks and the only other available space was Mr Froom's office. Normally a calm man, even his patience was tested when he returned from his vacation.

His usual morning greeting of, "What rubbish have you got for me today?" as he breezed into his office was closer to the truth than he could have imagined.

I learnt much from my experiences at The London, both when I was working there previously and when I was doing my holiday job.

It was clear even then in the '70s that this large London teaching hospital was under pressure, resources were stretched, but the dedication of those working there was humbling. There appeared to be this struggle to balance the requirements of the consultants, the nurses and the management. Less bureaucracy, less regulation and with political correctness not even a phrase, all working together for the good of the patients. It was a given, accepted by all. The words 'Mission Statement' had never entered the vocabulary.

After that first eventful holiday job followed a short interlude in Scotland where a dozen or so of us from Guy's, medics and dentists together, rented a farmhouse in Dumfries.

We travelled up in a variety of vehicles, including my mother's Hillman Imp, a peculiar little car with the engine in the boot.

Amongst us was one of the more flamboyant of our fellow students. An academic, Muriel was often adorned in bright eyeshadow and make-up, with an amazing variety of hot pants (the must-have fashion item of the day for the unabashed) that made her stand out amongst her peers at

Guy's. She was also gaining a reputation as being one of the more accident-prone students.

One morning, she turned up for a lecture with singed hair (it was already short) and eyebrows when a gas Bunsen burner had flared up as she omitted to light it in time.

On another occasion, she arrived dripping wet – she had been for a shower and forgot to take her towel with her and found the only way she could dry herself was on the roller towel in the washroom.

This was at the back of my mind when on the drive to Scotland; some of us shared the driving. She asked why I wasn't letting her drive my mother's car.

Eventually, I relented once we were safely on the narrow country lane leading to the farmhouse. "Turn right here," I said as we approached the long driveway through the surrounding fields. The car seemed to slow up and developed a dragging grating noise. I looked behind. Somehow, she had hooked the barbed-wire fence around the rear bumper and was pulling it up towards the farmhouse.

The farmer wasn't best pleased. We mended the fence whilst he rounded up his sheep.

It's moments like these that stay with me. The friendships we developed and even then, utilising our different skills and recognising the sensitivities, strengths and weaknesses in others has formed a foundation which I hope I have built on in the years beyond. Underscoring all this was humour and seeing the lighter moments in all aspects of life and people.

The start of our second year was the first for many who came straight from school with science A-levels. I guess that those of us who had done the foundation year felt we had a certain mature attitude, although, I hope, not a superior one.

The serious study began. There were three pre-clinical subjects: Biochemistry, Physiology and Anatomy. Knowledge in these subjects would give us an understanding of the human body and, it was hoped, equip us to practise our chosen profession.

Practical application in all the subjects formed a major part of the curriculum. Biochemistry, which explains the chemical processes related to living organisms, involved many hours spent in the laboratory. We worked in groups, usually paired up. Often, I joined one of the more delightfully flirtatious females, a friend from year one. We frequently exchanged bemused glances as neither of us could grasp how the experimentation was meant to proceed. This meant surreptitiously cribbing from the more enlightened in our year. Even in the midst of the stark surroundings of the chemistry lab, humour was never far away. I recall one such occasion. In an effort to underline the clinical significance of the experiments we were attempting to carry out, three large flagons of urine had been collected from the wards for us to analyse. This involved sucking up in a pipette (a glass tool with a chamber midway up for measuring liquid) small quantities of urine which we would then test. You remember Muriel, the accident-prone student from the Scottish holiday… unfortunately, she didn't remember to stop sucking when the pipette was full and took a large mouthful of urine. At least she didn't have to test for sugar content.

Physiology is a branch of biology and relates to the function of organs and organ systems. That could sound a heavy subject but in reality is a fascinating insight into how the body works. We were taught by Professor Macdonald, whose patient explanations helped enormously our understanding of this complex subject. In this, too, we carried out practical experiments, this time on each other.

One of the first experiments was a phenomenon called reactive hyperaemia. This involved obstructing the blood supply to the upper arm (similar to applying a tourniquet) and noting the reaction in the tissues that had been deprived of oxygen for varying lengths of time. It was very painful! That, however, was not the only and not very scientific conclusion. It did serve to demonstrate how valuable it is to experience sometimes what patients may be feeling so as to empathise with them and their anxieties. An important lesson for anyone in the caring professions.

Of all the subjects in the pre-clinical years, Anatomy for me was the most absorbing and fascinating. Anatomy could be taught by diagrams and textbooks and demonstrations using preserved anatomical specimens. This was in the days before CGI had ever been thought of, so for us, dissection was the most valuable.

We were divided into groups of six or so and each group allocated a body. Tutored by some excellent teachers under the auspices of one of the gurus of Anatomy, Professor Warwick, and helped by our 'Guide to Dissection', as aspiring dentists, we carried out detailed dissection of the head, neck and thorax (the upper part of the body). Although even in the grim environment of the dissecting room, humour was never far away, at no time was any disrespect evident in the way the bodies were handled.

An oxymoron, perhaps, but dead bodies brought the subject alive.

Anatomy was the only subject I ever came first in. I would like to think that this was due entirely to my abilities, but I suspect that the fact that the Anatomy examination was the day after a night of partying meant I may have been less hung-over than my fellow students.

As would-be dentists, we were taught comparative dental anatomy, comparing and contrasting the teeth of a variety of animal species. We looked in detail at the structure and composition of teeth which would, of course, be vital for us to know in the future.

So much depends on how the subjects were taught and who by. Our Dental Anatomy lecturer did have a certain charisma and Dental Anatomy became a popular subject, particularly amongst the female students.

Halfway through the course, we discovered another side to his talents. Thumbing through a glamour magazine, we stumbled upon a full-page picture of him (I have to add, in a tasteful pose and not revealing any of his personal anatomy). He had an alter ego as a male model.

The second year was another make-or-break year. Happily, unlike the struggle I had in the Foundation Year, I passed in all of the subjects.

THREE

THE CLINICAL YEARS

Next came the clinical years. We were beginning to feel like dentists.

Dentistry is not just a single subject. Like medicine with all its different specialties, so too has dentistry its own subspecialties. Ahead of us lay three more years of study. We would cover a range of subjects, including general medicine, surgery, anaesthetics, histology, pathology and pharmacology. Sometimes the subjects would overlap; the purely dental subjects would be taught in great detail.

Before we were let loose on patients, there was much preparation and learning.

Dentistry is obviously a very hands-on subject. In medicine, it was always said you could tell the difference between a Guy's man and a Bart's man. A Guy's man would examine a patient with one hand in his pocket and a Bart's man with both hands in his pockets. In dentistry, we never had that luxury afforded to us.

It was also said that you could always tell a Guy's man, but you couldn't tell him much. Notice the emphasis on the male role! Unlike a student in the 1970s, which were predominantly male years, there are more female graduates now than males. A welcome change.

A common perception is that a dentist's life is largely one of drilling and filling teeth. I hope to show that this is not an accurate description any longer of a profession that had its origins in the days of barber surgeons. It did seem apt, however, that our first real introduction to clinical dentistry should be to teach us the basics of 'drilling and filling'.

In year three, our first experience of clinical dentistry was not on patients but on so-called 'phantom heads'. These models replicated the human jaws with real teeth (extracted elsewhere in the hospital) and were anatomically correct. Having said that, it was a very artificial set-up, no cheeks, no tongue, no saliva and no feeling! And so, we learnt the fundamentals of the science of dentistry. Placing a filling in a tooth is not the haphazard affair that many may think. There are, or were, believe it or not, principles of cavity design and preparation originally described by an illustrious American dentist by the name of G.V. Black way back in the 19th century. But surely dentistry had moved on! Any scientific development, and this is particularly true in medicine and dentistry, is an evolutionary process. Anatomical and biological considerations are paramount but so too is the ability to adapt to progress in dental materials as research yields results. Uppermost in everyone's mind was and remains the well-being of the patient.

Were we well equipped when confronted with our first patient? Practising on phantom heads and learning to administer a local anaesthetic injection in an orange may have had its lighter moments, but all of us felt a degree of trepidation when confronted with our first real live patient. For once, it was us as budding dentists who were more nervous than our patients.

I do remember my first patient (I think most of us do). Mrs Jackson, a single mother from South London, looking older than her years, who already had a number of filled teeth. After an exhausting three hours for myself and Mrs Jackson, I had successfully placed a further filling to add to her grand total.

Three hours for the patient but even longer for me as a student. This was the early 1970s and although the high-speed drill had been commonplace in dental practices for several years, in the dental school they were still in short supply. To guarantee one and one that would work, meant arriving an hour ahead of the appointment.

I felt a sense of achievement after that first patient. At least I remembered she was not a phantom head unlike one fellow student. Rather than using an air syringe to dry the teeth before placing a filling, he, forgetting the patient was a real person, blew into her mouth!

We gradually gained confidence, I hope both in ourselves but more importantly the hard-won confidence of our patients, many of whom, after hours in the dental chair, we got to know well.

From early on, I guess because of the many hours I spent with them, I became aware that these were not simply teeth to be filled but patients to be treated, each with their own stories to tell. Such a diverse range of patients even in those first few months. From teachers to policemen, vicars, postmen, engineers, builders and plumbers. Every trade and profession must have been represented. But all had one thing in common: tolerant and understanding, with very few complaining.

Each stage of our treatment was supervised and checked and 'signed off'. This was carried out by clinical demonstrators (I would in time become one myself) who scrutinised, criticised and sometimes applauded our treatment. But most importantly, they passed on to us their experience and skills in a way textbooks never could.

We helped each other, mostly when we faced some potential disaster that we needed to avoid. Much of the time these were clinical difficulties but not always. "I have a problem with my patient." Yvonne, a fellow student, had a worried and somewhat embarrassed look on her face.

"What sort of problem?" I asked.

"You'd better come and see, and it's not his teeth." Clearly, Yvonne's sensual and sensitive side had, figuratively speaking, rubbed off on her young adolescent patient. The bulge in his trousers was unmissable.

"What are you planning for him?" I asked.

"A filling," she replied. "No more than that."

"Have you given him a local anaesthetic?" I asked.

"No, not yet," she replied.

"Best not then," I said. That was probably our first real use of distraction therapy.

Part of our teaching included the anatomical form of each tooth. It was this shape that we tried to replicate when carving our amalgam fillings for our patients. Amalgam is a strange material, essentially a mixture of metal powder and mercury which went through a plastic phase when it could be carved to the desired shape. I shudder to think how these components were literally amalgamated together. Firstly mixed with a pestle and mortar and then the excess mercury was squeezed out by hand through a piece of gauze. No wonder, then, that we had samples of our hair and nails taken to ensure we were not suffering from mercury poisoning. Having said this, it was a great material to work with and gave great service to countless patients over many many years. It was a very forgiving material – it was said you could do an amalgam filling under water and still get a good result. For patients it was safe and effective but nowadays has been superseded by a whole new range of other materials, each with their own challenges, but none so forgiving.

We progressed from fillings to crowns and for this we were taught the laboratory procedures and techniques. This meant that we were personally responsible for every aspect of the patients' treatment. This would be so vital in the years to come.

Apart from treating our own patients, there were regular demonstrations when we were shown how to perform procedures. Usually, this involved us crowding round the hapless patient as the treatment was carried out by one of the clinical lecturers. Medical students had similar observation domes above the operating theatres, until this practice ended when it became clear that relatives of patients were also viewing the progress of operations on their loved ones.

There were mishaps when the treatment did not go quite according to plan. On one occasion, a student craning to get a better view leant on the flush button for the suction, resulting in the patient's mouth filling up rather than emptying out and with what is best left unsaid.

Our clinical studies began in the old dental school at Guy's, which had not changed since the 1950s. Then came a transformation as we moved into Guy's Tower, opened by the Queen in 1974, where the dental school occupied the top ten floors of the thirty-storey building, the tallest building in London at the time.

Each floor had a separate department or specialty, and floors twenty-five and twenty-six were devoted to Conservative Dentistry – this was not a political term (like, I suppose, the Labour Ward) but described that aspect of dentistry devoted to conserving a patient's dentition (teeth). Being so high up over London was an obvious distraction. In-between patients, we would take in the stunning views, the river Thames and the boats, cars, trains and people, dwarf-like figures on the streets below. But tragedy also stalked the capital. I remember one occasion when an IRA bomb exploded on a train just beneath us as it carried commuters in from the suburbs.

Most of our patients came from South London and for us, there was no shortage. There were long waiting lists for treatment, all of it provided free although, of course, requiring a considerable investment in the patients' time.

We had some outstanding teachers, both clinicians and technical staff, who guided us at the beginning of our long journey to graduation. We rotated through the different specialties and early on we gained an insight into all the varied options available to us. But at this stage, we had to develop an understanding, if not a detailed knowledge, of each subject. We learnt the principles of general medicine, surgery and pharmacology which, together with our clinical attachments, reinforced the importance of the holistic approach to patient care.

Our breaks offered a welcome relief from the pressures that we were all beginning to feel. We chatted about our experiences, exchanged ideas and practical tips, which in many ways were as valuable as the formal teaching. These lunch breaks were an important catch-up time. We queued up in the 'Spit', the in-house canteen, where the menu changed daily. I remember one occasion in particular. Rose, a catering assistant from South London with fiery red hair to match her temperament, asked the guy in front of me what he wanted. He perused the menu. "I'll have the pissoles, please, Rose," he said.

"What do you mean, 'pissoles'?" she asked.

"That's what it says here," he said, showing Rose the typed menu.

"That's not a 'P'," she said. "It's an 'R'."

"Oh, okay then," he said. "I'll have the arseholes."

And so, amongst the serious study, humour was never far away, and it was our life blood, as it would continue to be.

Prosthetics formed an important part of our course. This is where we cut our teeth, so to speak, in learning the clinical and technical aspects of constructing dentures. Patient demand for dentures to replace missing teeth was high, and there were long waiting lists that we as students worked our way through. More people then had more missing teeth than now, and treatment outside of the hospital was expensive. There was no-one-size-fits all approach. All the dentures were painstakingly constructed, and we were guided in this by an array of teachers, both dentists and technicians, because back then we not only carried out the clinical aspects, such as impression taking, but also constructed the dentures in the laboratory.

Art and science came together in comfortable cohesion. Patients wanted to look good but also wanted to be able to chew their food comfortably and effectively, and so our ability to achieve these desired results was often tested to the extreme. And tested literally when the exams came around. As part of the examination process, we had to make complete dentures for patients with no teeth of their own, and partial dentures where only some teeth were missing. Each stage of the process was scrutinised by an examiner. We used to sneak our patients in before the exam to ensure they were happy with the result and make final adjustments out of sight of the examiner. This was especially crucial at the so-called try-in stage of complete dentures when a mock-up in wax had been constructed by us in the laboratory. The dentures were finished, but rather than the teeth being fixed to the plastic or acrylic plate, they were set in wax and tried in the patient's mouth to ensure comfort, fit and, most importantly, appearance.

We nervously viewed our patients and, if mutually satisfied, the patient would be sent away for an hour to then return to face the closer scrutiny of the examiner.

An unfortunate fellow student, deliriously happy with his result, dismissed his patient with the words 'go and have a coffee', without removing the waxed-up denture from the patient's mouth. The patient returned with the teeth floating in a molten mix of wax and coffee. A mistake not repeated again!

Of the patients I saw in those student years, two stick in my mind. One was a delightful elderly Irishman. I provided him with new complete upper and lower dentures. As was customary, he was given an appointment to return the following week for any adjustments. "How are you getting on?" I asked.

"Grand," he said. "I have to say, these are the finest dentures I have ever had."

"Are they comfortable then?" I asked.

"Oh, I am not wearing them," he said. "They are too good for that!"

The other patient I recall was not so easily satisfied. Week after week, he returned saying his dentures were too tight and uncomfortable. Eventually, the clinical demonstrator overseeing his treatment was equally exasperated. "As far as I can see," he said to me, out of earshot of the patient, "they are fitting very well. Let me try one more thing."

He went over to the patient and, appearing to examine the dentures carefully, suddenly exclaimed, "I can see what's wrong; you've been given the wrong size – there must have been a mix-up. These are size six, you need a seven." He went off and carefully engraved in the denture the figure seven and proudly presented them to the patient to show him.

He tried them in. "Perfect fit," said the patient. "I knew they were the wrong size." We never saw him again.

We rotated between the various departments in an organised fashion. We were not responsible for looking after the patient's entire care. The downside of this approach meant that our treatments were focused specifically on which department we were in. The grandly titled department for Periodontology and Preventive Dentistry was responsible for the patient's gum health and was also where the dental hygienists, overwhelmingly female, were trained, which added to the attraction of the department.

Under the guidance of two eminent professors, Ronald Emslie and Tony Naylor, we were taught a whole range of skills from surgery to scaling to help patients improve their gum health, retain their teeth and hopefully achieve one of the raisons d'être of the dental profession.

We would go to the waiting room and call our patients. On occasions, fictitious patients were inserted on our list, particularly on those of the gullible members of our group. "Mustafa Scale," one student called out; the only response was a ripple of laughter before he retreated red-faced to hide his blushes.

Names throughout the ages have always been a source of humour and confusion, and other examples have followed me in my professional life as we will see later.

During these clinical attachments, I was still living in the student hall at Ealing, and a pattern of life there seemed to develop.

Yes, there was plenty of studying but always time for those extra-curricular activities that form part of student life, then, as it is today. One unexpected obstacle to studying, although not to the other activities, was the three-day week imposed by the government during the long-running miners' dispute in 1972. Plunged into darkness for several hours every week as the electricity supply was switched off to conserve power up and down the country, we scrutinised the rota published in the evening paper to see when our street would be in darkness. The novelty of studying by candlelight rapidly lost its appeal, so we abandoned our books to more convivial tasks like walking to the pub and other activities that didn't require light!

At Guy's, we rotated through all the different specialties, learning a variety of procedures and techniques and gaining an in-depth clinical understanding of the complexities of oral health and its impact on different age groups. From paediatric dentistry and orthodontics to oral surgery and oral medicine, we were being equipped with a variety of skills and gained the confidence needed to practise in the outside world. Not that this journey was free of pitfalls. The teaching we had and those delivering it were generally exceptional, if somewhat intimidating to the inexperienced student.

Restorative dentistry (the bread and butter of many future graduates) was led by Professor Rowe, an impressive teacher with a wealth of knowledge and dry sense of humour. He would patrol the clinic, peering into the gaping mouths of patients, often questioning what exactly was being done in the name of science. One unfortunate encounter I had was when, heating some soft wax over a Bunsen burner in order to take a record of a patient's bite, he loomed over me and said, in his mildly sarcastic tone, "Did you know your sleeve is on fire?" Unknown to me, the sleeve of my white coat was smouldering nicely.

I never imagined myself as disruptive, but that may not have been the view of some of the teachers. Oral medicine –

which encompasses the whole range of so-called soft tissue conditions affecting the mouth, from the innocuous but painful mouth ulcers to the rarer mouth cancers, together with the signs of general illness that can appear in the mouth – fascinated me. Ronald Cawson was the Professor of Oral Medicine, a much-revered and respected clinician who would regularly give lectures. In those days, there was a virtual one hundred per cent attendance and we listened attentively… or should have done. If you were not paying attention, it must not be obvious. I flouted this basic rule by telling a joke to a fellow student. "What's so funny?" Professor Cawson pointedly asked me.

"I'm sorry, I was just telling a joke."

"Then share it," he said. And I did, although the joke itself has been lost in the annals of time. The laughter was at my expense. My humiliation was funnier than my joke.

One of the most important aspects of medicine and dentistry is making the initial diagnosis before treatment can be started. Many times, it is obvious, but there are occasions in dentistry when the cause may not be clear. Most important is to listen to the patient and pass the answers to this history and the clinical examination through a virtual 'surgical sieve'. To this end, patients were invited to attend to be examined as part of the students' clinical qualifying exams. This was always a balance as some patients, taking their instructions not to help the students literally, would remain tight-lipped, proverbially and in reality. You prayed you would not have an obstructive patient.

When I was called to sit my clinical examination, I could not believe my luck. I had just finished a clinical attachment in Oral Surgery, assisting a wonderful Oral Surgeon, David MacDonald, a dour Scotsman with tremendous clinical skills and a calm demeanour. I had assisted in theatres when a young male patient had been admitted with a large cyst in his lower jaw that needed removing.

There, staring at me in the examination, was the self-same patient, having made a full recovery from his surgery. I asked him the questions (already knowing the answers), examined him and made what I knew was the correct diagnosis. The patient had 'a dentigerous cyst surgically enucleated'.

I presented my findings to the two examiners. One was an eminent Maxillofacial Surgeon, Professor Sowray from another teaching hospital. I started by describing the patient's history and symptoms. "What's the patient's name?" he asked me.

"Name?" I said.

"Yes," he said. "He has a name."

I knew his date of birth, presenting symptoms, history, diagnosis and treatment. I did not know his name. I failed the examination.

I was shattered, but that taught me a most important lesson and one which I have never forgotten. Although not realising it at the time, Professor Sowray did me a great service. Patients all have their own individual identities; they are not simply conditions to be treated.

I resat the examination and, on that occasion, passed. It's all in the name.

As we progressed, we had further clinical attachments in General Anaesthetic clinics and in Dental Casualty, as it was then known. During the attachment in Dental

Casualty, we learnt many additional skills. Often, patients would attend with serious infections. This was a time when antibiotics were often administered by injection into the bottom. Chaperoned by Mrs Clare, a senior dental nurse who ran Dental Casualty rather like a headmistress runs a school, we would cautiously and carefully inject into the patient's buttock. Or most of us would. One delightful student in his strong Chinese accent would, as a preamble to administering the antibiotic, announce to the patient and all in earshot (which was most of those in the Casualty Unit): "Just a quick prick in bum!"

Back in the '70s, general anaesthetics using nitrous oxide were administered to outpatients in a dental chair, a practice wisely curtailed due to a number of anaesthetic tragedies. It was my least favourite attachment and was reminiscent of the old style of dentistry that we were thankfully moving away from. It seemed brutal at the time and patients often felt nauseous and were violently sick after these procedures. Even then, we had our lighter moments. One of the oral surgeons, known for shouting instructions to his students, bellowed as I struggled to remove an upper front tooth, "Screw it, lad, screw it, surely you know how to screw!", a technique I have practised many times since!

It was at about this time, still living in the student hall in the leafy suburbs of Ealing, that my life changed.

To say Judy breezed into my life was not quite the way it happened. But the arrival of Judy and her identical twin sister Sally felt like a breath of fresh air. They joined their elder sister Sue whom I'd already struck up a good friendship with and who had been living in the hall for a year. The twins both had this electrifying personality and sense of fun and humour that was irresistible. Romance came later.

I remember one particular occasion, a few months after Judy had arrived, when we were meeting up with a fellow dental student Belinda and her boyfriend Alan at their flat in Streatham. We drove over there in Judy's Austin A30, which her father had had repainted a bright canary yellow. It had originally belonged to her ninety-five-year-old grandmother who was persuaded to give up driving after she ignored a roundabout and drove straight across it. But we were not alone. Unknown to our friends, Judy's twin Sally had joined us. She stayed in the car until halfway through the evening when she swapped with Judy, the change going completely unnoticed as the music of Cat Stevens' 'Tea for the Tillerman' blared out from the record player. As the record came to an end, Judy rejoined us from the bathroom where she had been hiding to the utter bewilderment of Alan and Belinda and our astonishment that the prank had worked.

Driving a bright yellow car could be a disadvantage and we were stopped on a number of occasions by the police. Once, driving up the A12 to Suffolk, we were pulled over and Judy, as the driver, was told to get out of the car. "We need to carry out some checks," the officer announced. One of the checks involved ensuring that the handbrake worked (which we knew it didn't). I remained sitting in the passenger seat as the two officers pushed the car from behind to check. Fortunately, and without them noticing, I managed to extend my leg onto the driver's side and press the footbrake. They were satisfied. Next came the indicator check. As an old car, there were no flashing indicator lights but rather a little lever-like arm that swung out from the bodywork. Unfortunately, it frequently jammed, but a sturdy blow with my hand (again unnoticed by the officers) released it and we were on our way.

Most students stayed at the Ealing Hall for a year, two at most. Somehow, I managed four years. In my final year, I moved into a student hall at Guy's, one of the first residents in this new accommodation block. With one exception, it was a perfect arrangement. The exception was Judy, who had gone to live with her sisters in a flat in Westbourne Park. By then, I was falling in love.

What had begun as a friendship was rapidly developing into something more serious. Judy was a very special person, attractive and such fun to be with, and I felt myself being drawn towards her. We laughed a lot, talked a lot and started doing things together, just the two of us. We both shared a love of the theatre. I missed her when she wasn't there.

This, I knew, was who I wanted to share my life with.

Our finals were rapidly approaching. We had to select and have approved patients who would be our clinical cases for the examination. I was fortunate that a student in the year below offered to be my 'guinea pig', but this was only one part of the examination that was both written and practical and spread over several days. I opted to do two separate finals examinations as an insurance against failure. One was for the diploma awarded by the Royal College of Surgeons and the other, a short while later, was for the degree awarded by the University of London.

FOUR

GRADUATION AND BEYOND

The exams themselves all these years later are a bit of a blur but not the aftermath. The results were posted on a board outside the Royal College of Surgeons, a grandiose imposing edifice lying on the south side of Lincoln's Inn Fields, the largest public square in London. We all gathered there and crowded around the board, some more reluctant than others to see the results. Smiles, shouts, tears and laughter filled the early summer air. I had passed! Delirious with excitement, six of us piled into a friend's Morris Minor Convertible. First stop was Bride Lane, off Fleet Street, where I was to tell Judy the good news. Turning into Bride Lane, a policeman stepped in front of the car and, in the time-honoured way policemen always seem to speak, enquired of the driver,

"Afternoon, sir. Do you realise you are 'eaded down a one-way street in the wrong direction, an offence contrary to the traffic regulations?"

"I am sorry, Officer," said the driver, "but we have just passed our finals!"

"Congratulations, sir, you better be on your way then!"

Although I could legally register and practise, as some did, I stayed and completed my degree. This gave me an additional qualification, although the syllabus was virtually identical. The exam followed a similar format and, thankfully, so did the results. A whole new world was opening up.

First, though, came the graduation ceremony in the prestigious surroundings of the Royal College of Surgeons. Founded in 1800, it is a grade II* listed building where we, together with medical graduates, received our diplomas in traditional fashion, doffing our caps in front of an array of multicoloured gowned figures, the great and the good of the medical and dental hierarchy.

It was, however, the graduation ceremony at the University of London, held at the Royal Albert Hall, that made the greatest impact as the Chancellor at the time was the Queen Mother. And so, it was a moment of great pride for me and my parents when she awarded me my degree. It would be many years before I donned a cap and gown again.

In those days, to practise as a dental surgeon you could simply put up a brass plate and open a practice. Unlike medical graduates, there was no compulsory period of doing a 'house job', i.e. working as a junior doctor in hospital. It was, however, considered a good way to enhance your skills and help you decide which direction or specialty you wished to follow.

Applying for a house surgeon position was competitive, particularly at your own teaching hospital. I remember submitting applications to Guy's and various other hospitals and attending what seemed like gruelling interviews, much like an extension of the examination process. I had my sights set on a job at Guy's. I knew the consultants and the system, and I had loved my time as a student there and had planned to embark on my career at my alma mater.

I waited through the hot summer months until a letter came, offering me a job as a house surgeon at The London Hospital, another establishment I knew well from working there in my previous life. The job offer was held for just twenty-four hours and I had not heard from Guy's. Cautious by nature, so strong was my desire to work at Guy's, I took a gamble, declined the offer and waited. In what was the hottest summer for many years, I sweated for another reason. And the list of house surgeon appointments was published, and there was my name – I had been successful.

In August 1976, I was appointed house surgeon to Professors Emslie and Naylor, who were consultant periodontists and encompassing other duties that ranged from clinical supervision of students, working in Dental Casualty and providing emergency cover for the maxillofacial surgeons at weekends, with stints in the main hospital's A&E Department.

That first day, wearing our white coats proudly displaying our 'House Surgeon' name badge, we felt we had made it. Able to treat patients without supervision, prescribe drugs and supervise others myself, and the newly appointed house surgeons were very much thrust into the deep end of clinical dentistry. But we soon realised that what we had gained in knowledge we would lack in experience. We would gather at lunchtimes and over coffee, seeking reassurance and guidance from each other. Gradually, we gained confidence, but our limitations were all too obvious.

One patient I recall was a grossly obese female whom I had been asked to see. She had been fitted with fixed wires on her teeth, preventing her from opening her mouth to eat as part of a strict dietary regime. Unfortunately, it was causing her great distress and I was asked to remove them. Having only observed the placement of these wires by maxillofacial surgeons in the treatment of jaw fractures, I was completely at a loss.

Fortunately, help came not in the form of the cavalry but from the navy. On attachment was a naval surgeon lieutenant who deftly carried out the procedure, not one I was ever likely to repeat. It also struck me that there cannot be too many overweight sailors in the navy.

My time in Dental Casualty was the most testing and where pressure was greatest. Most patients came because they were in pain; many were irregular attenders and were very anxious. A few were time-wasters. Reassurance, sympathy and time (which was in short supply) were what was needed. Firstly, careful questioning and history-taking to ascertain the cause of the symptoms. One would think it was easy, but toothache and facial pain has so many causes, its origin is often not obvious. Even here, especially here, we had our lighter moments. The patient who is convinced radio transmitters have been inserted into his amalgam fillings and no amount of reassurance will convince him otherwise. But not to listen and just dismiss his fantastical belief would be to do that patient a disservice. Recognising what was beyond my capability was an important part of the learning experience. 'Treat all patients the same and with dignity'. This was more challenging when the patient was a prisoner handcuffed to the dental chair. Not helped when the accompanying warder fainted at the sight of blood.

And there were, sadly, the incessant time-wasters. Patients who may have been lonely or just anxious. Their notes were sometimes marked with PPP: Paracetamol, Penicillin and Piss off. This was not a practice I continued. Communication skills come with experience. Clear explanations must leave no room for doubt. A young female patient presented with an abscess affecting an upper front tooth. This required draining, a procedure that entailed placing a rubber dam (a rubber sheet) over the tooth to isolate it from the rest of the mouth in order to prevent contamination and enable the safe use of fine instruments. Explaining to the patient I was about to put on a rubber protective was not the most sensible thing to have said. I didn't blame her for exiting the surgery rapidly.

Cover at weekends brought its own surprises. Two of us would generally be on duty dealing with all sorts of dental emergencies. The usual array of patients would include those suffering from facial swellings, post-extraction bleeding and, sometimes, very serious infections that would require admission to hospital under the maxillofacial surgeons. On one occasion, Belinda – my good friend and confidante from our first day at Guy's – and I were on duty and our bleep (which we were required to carry in order to be instantly contactable) went off. She took the call and went to A&E, where she was told a female patient was having discomfort from an upper denture. Hardly a serious emergency and surely not one necessitating a visit to the hard-pressed A&E Department. Never take at face value what you hear. The patient was indeed in considerable discomfort; the offending denture was stuck in the wrong orifice. Apparently, her partner had sneezed at an inopportune moment! "Summon the Gynae on-call," was Belinda's parting shot. "Wrong end!"

Part of the role of a junior house surgeon was to supervise students carrying out treatment. For my part, this was mainly overseeing patients having restorative treatment such as fillings, crowns and bridges and root treatments. Bearing in mind many of the students were themselves nearing qualification, there would be times when they were the ones who had greater skills and knowledge, or so it seemed. But there were moments when one felt one did make a small contribution to their education. All treatment carries potential risks, but so many safeguards are in place to prevent catastrophic episodes. However, there was one occasion when a pale, distraught student rushed up to me. He had been drilling a tooth in preparation for a filling when the bur attached to the drill fractured and was lost. The biggest concern was that the fractured fragment could be inhaled or lodged in the patient's trachea (windpipe). A strict protocol was in place, requiring an immediate chest X-ray to exclude the possibility of inhalation. This came back clear; the area around the dentist's chair was searched but still no sign of the errant fragment.

Finally, I carried out a further examination of the patient. There, embedded in the folds under the tongue, was the missing fragment. All was well, but a cautionary tale and a lesson learnt.

Those first six months gave me the grounding I required. The opportunity to develop my skills and interests were helped enormously not just by the consultants to whom we were attached but from the camaraderie, exchange of ideas and reassurances from one's fellow house surgeons.

That first job flew past, and I was already thinking of where next. I loved working in a hospital and had planned to apply for a house surgeon post at a different hospital in oral surgery. I travelled to Cambridge for an interview at Addenbrook's, but my preference was to stay in London. Just as well, as my application was unsuccessful. Working as a house surgeon in oral surgery at a non-teaching hospital would require a considerable commitment with an on-call rota shared amongst you and a registrar. In the midst of these interviews, an unexpected opportunity arose. A phone call alerted me to a vacancy that had arisen at Guy's. A unique role, that of InPatient Dental Officer, was listed for appointment.

The first hurdle was the requirement for at least one year's post-qualification experience, which I didn't meet. I thought I would give it a go and applied. The interview seemed to go well. I felt I was back at school in the headmaster's study interviewed by Mr Vale, the hospital's 'Dental Superintendent'. Immaculately dressed in a grey suit with a mirror finish on his shoes, he was an imposing and somewhat intimidating presence in my student years. A decision was imminent. Meanwhile, another interview, at the Central Middlesex Hospital, had gone well. This was another surprise! I think the fact I was then into home-brewing may have clinched it. I used to brew my own beer and the consultant interviewing me must have had a similar hobby as we spoke about it at length. Offered a job, you don't turn it down easily. I asked for twenty-four hours to consider. The next day came the call. I had been appointed InPatient Dental Officer by Guy's. This role was for three days a week; it came with its own dental surgery in the main hospital, a dedicated dental nurse and a workload which a seven-day week would not do justice to.

Responsible for the dental care of hospital inpatients in the Guy's group of hospitals, it included the regular screening of patients booked for cardiac surgery to ensure dental fitness before their operations so as to minimise the risk of infection, as well as dealing with dental emergencies as they arose on the wards. In addition to seeing patients at Guy's, I also had access to a hospital car to drive to the far-flung hospitals in the Guy's group. A whole new world opened up.

Issued with a hospital bleep, I would visit wards to see patients who were too poorly to be brought to my surgery. On occasions, I would provide treatment whilst the patients would remain confined to their beds, but most would come to me. Many were awaiting major open-heart surgery, in those days still in its relative infancy, and the stoicism and humour they displayed made a big impression on me that has stayed with me always.

Images of three patients have also remained with me over the years from my days working at Guy's. The first was a young woman, Moya, who was a long-term psychiatric patient in the York Clinic, the self-contained psychiatric wing at Guy's Hospital. She had multiple mental health problems, but I was asked to see her because of severe acid erosion of her teeth which was a consequence of frequent vomiting associated with bulimia. Sometimes, I used to visit her in the York Clinic, but more often she would come and see me in my surgery. I think she enjoyed this more as it took her away from the confinement of the clinic.

Over time I got to know her, and I think and hope she trusted me. Sometimes she would appear withdrawn and insular and at other times could become more animated. I often wonder whether she recovered and that what I witnessed was the flickering of some hope for her future.

Whilst at Guy's, I gained so much from seeing patients with their own difficulties. This undoubtedly helped me in my years in practice. Many years later when I was in practice, I had the rather unusual experience of seeing as a patient an eminent psychiatrist, a delightful kind and compassionate man, and then discovering that another of my patients, who was on the autistic spectrum, had been under his care. Artistic and talented in many ways, we got to know each other over the years. He would travel to London for his appointments, often with his assistance dog who would lay protectively at his side during treatment, giving him that extra confidence that he required. He was warm and generous in his conversation. One day, he asked if over the Christmas period he could come and spend some hours in the practice, taking photos of London through my surgery window. He had already presented me with a photo of the Post Office Tower with my name miraculously in the banner at the top!

So, he came and spent time in the practice taking pictures, going away and retouching them so as to stamp his own identity on the images. One was so striking and in my mind summed up what I hoped was an impression shared by others that my surgery was an oasis of tranquillity in the midst of the hustle and bustle of London. It was published in the *British Dental Journal*. The picture showed a view through the large floor-to-ceiling window in my practice of a typical London scene, with the Post Office Tower in the background. In the foreground was my balcony, often adorned with plants and flowers carefully tended by my nurse. She was proud of her balcony garden with its colourful display of geraniums, fuchsias, narcissi and lavender which, even in London, attracted bees. Sometimes, some of the keen gardeners amongst my patients would add their contributions either by bringing plants or even getting on their knees to do some impromptu gardening. In front of my window were two wicker chairs where I would often sit with patients before seating them in the dental chair. The impression it created was one, I hoped, of calm and was far less threatening than the perception that patients often have of the dental chair.

I remember many years previously, an anxious patient sat in my chair and as I was about to start treatment, he firmly gripped what he thought was the armrest. "Mr Martin," I said, somewhat urgently, "please let go of my leg!"

Memories of two other patients from my time at Guy's stay with me.

A lady from South London was referred to me prior to undergoing open-heart surgery. She required a full dental clearance (all her teeth extracted) and their replacement with complete dentures before her operation. Even under normal circumstances, this would be stressful enough, but with the prospect of heart surgery as well, many could not have coped. She was remarkable, remaining stoic throughout and retaining her South London sense of humour. I was also humbled by the gratitude she showed. I felt that gratitude was misplaced but for me, it showed that even in the face of adversity, there were people like her who seem to think of others rather than themselves. A lesson in life.

A third patient had to have emergency dental treatment prior to having open-heart surgery. He had been on the waiting list for heart surgery for some time and the date was fast approaching. I had expected to see him after his operation. Sadly, he didn't survive. That, too, had an impact.

There were lighter moments as well. A call to a ward to see Mr Arthur Ritis turned out to be a patient with arthritis; my nurse at the time, a cheerful young woman from the East End, wrote it as it was spoke.

One hospital I used to visit was St Olave's in Rotherhithe, where to venture out after dark back in the '70s was akin to taking your life in your own hands. Every fortnight, I would hold a clinic for patients there. This was a welcome respite from the buzz of Guy's and where the pace was slower. And the patient I saw covered in tattoos from head to toe, was he really Al Capone's driver as he claimed?

Interspersed with my clinical duties were informal seminars that I gave to the nurses, stressing to them the importance of the oral health of the patients on their wards, which understandably was not exactly at the top of their list of priorities. I hope I at least conveyed to them the importance of avoiding the apocryphal misfortune of the nurse who collected all the dentures in a bowl from patients in order to clean them, only then to be faced with the monumental task of returning them to their rightful owners.

As I was only committed to three days a week at Guy's, I had to seek work elsewhere. And so, I ended up at the Thamesmead Health Centre at the heart of a new housing development in what was then a depressed area of South London. I used to drive there and park in the underground car park until one of my colleagues, on returning to her car one evening, found it full of water as a fire hose had been discharged into the interior. From then on, I parked at a local factory and walked.

There, I saw patients from deprived backgrounds, adults and children. One child I remember, a lad around eight or nine, came and sat in my chair. "Have you just come from school?"

"No," he replied. "I've just had feet ferapy." I then told him the merits of keeping his teeth as healthy as his feet. He looked mystified. "Wot 'ave my feet got to do with it?" he asked.

"Haven't you just had them treated?" I said.

"No," he said. "Feet ferapy." It then dawned on me he had been seeing the speech therapist. That put me firmly in my place.

Well-run, well-equipped, dedicated staff and colleagues all willing to share and impart their knowledge and skills, though this episode went unremarked by me.

Marrying Judy in 1978, I gained a whole new family. As well as her twin, Judy had three sisters and, together with their husbands, there grew a special bond that was to last all our lives. In the years that followed, we had two wonderful daughters, Clare and Abi, and our lives changed forever. The joy and happiness overwhelmed us.

Judy's father John was a country GP in a village in Cambridgeshire, with his practice attached to his home. Loved by his patients, a true gentleman, kind, compassionate and never one to turn his patients away. I aspired to be like him. The only defence against the over-demanding and difficult patients, who would have a habit of appearing at evenings and weekends, was his wife. My mother-in-law, the epitome of fair play, would, however, stand no nonsense and certainly not time-wasters at 11pm at night.

Every practice will have their difficult and demanding patients. One such patient of my father-in-law was Mrs Buzzy. She would phone up frequently at weekends and John was always polite to her and never rushed her, but even he felt the strain. One weekend, sitting down for Sunday lunch, the phone rang. John answered and half an hour later rejoined us for lunch. "It was bloody Mrs Buzzy again," he said.

With us for lunch and listening was our four-year-old niece (who herself would become a doctor). Half an hour later, the phone rang again. Our niece ran to pick it up and, handing it to my father-in-law, shouted down the receiver, "It's bloody Mrs Buzzy!" From then on, I had a name for my difficult patients.

My career was to take a different direction, but in those early days of married life, I was still at Guy's. Whilst working there, I became a patient myself in the hospital and I was admitted to the surgical ward adjacent to where my dental surgery was. I was to undergo a fairly major procedure on my oesophagus to relieve a problem I had with swallowing, a condition known as achalasia. This experience as a patient taught me a great deal.

Much to my relief, the registrar Bill Owen, assisting the consultant surgeon, was one of the clinical demonstrators who taught me and my fellow students Anatomy, so at least he knew his way around. He was a delightful, caring competent surgeon who sadly died young.

Although my operation was a success, I remained in hospital for three weeks. Perhaps by virtue of being on the hospital staff, I had the luxury of my own room. Visitors were frequent, with other patients popping in as they passed my room. One in particular I remember; a middle-aged man in his stripy pyjamas walked in and, in conspiratorial tones, said, whilst he pulled down his pyjama bottoms, "'Ere, 'ave a look at this – it's never been so big – the wife's going to be delighted." Obviously, some unintended consequence of a surgical procedure he had just undergone.

It was clear who was in charge on the wards, especially in the early mornings as the ward awakened. Maud was the ward cleaner, armed with her mop and bucket, anyone who crossed the demarcation zone from dry to wet did so at their peril. She would shout in her local East End dialect, "Get off me bleeding floor." Consultants waiting to do their ward rounds would quiver in their shoes and wait until the floor had dried when Maud would sound her all clear.

The staff worked hard but even back then they were hard-pressed, short-staffed and under pressure, and occasionally, patience snapped. The laundry ran out of linen as a result of some minor industrial dispute, and we slept in paper sheets. As a patient, you rapidly lost your inhibitions.

Laughter was never far away. As I had my own room, I was afforded the benefit of a small black and white TV set. One evening, I tuned in to watch Mike Leigh's *Abigail's Party*, a black comedy with, amongst others, Alison Steadman. Not only did it raise my spirits, so hilarious did I find it that I nearly burst my stitches. Come to think of it, maybe this is where the expression 'in stitches' comes from.

Before long, I was back on my feet. But my absence gave me the time to reflect on my future and which direction I was to follow. Much as I enjoyed the buzz of hospital life, I was no academic, and the thought of further study and examinations as I settled into married life persuaded me to seek alternatives. General practice was clearly an option, but for me, the thought of NHS treadmill dentistry had little appeal.

As so often happens, opportunities arise when you least expect them. One day, I was in the dental hospital discussing a patient's X-ray with the Consultant Radiologist, when he casually remarked that a friend and colleague of his, who was clinical dental advisor to a dental company, was looking for a dentist to run the dental practice at the company's head office in London's Soho. I went for an interview and was offered a part-time position running a dental practice for staff working there. In addition, there would be other tasks, such as helping with the evaluation of new dental materials.

When I say running the dental practice, this was not entirely accurate. Sheila Peters, a married woman in her forties, was my dental nurse. She ran the practice. In her clear, direct, efficient manner, she mothered me, even resisting the temptation to put 'L' plates round my neck when a patient asked whether I was really a dentist or just an apprentice. We laughed a lot in those days. Referred to by Sheila as the 'oracle' because of the words of wisdom he uttered, Alan Atkinson, the head of clinical services, would appear from time to time with a request for me to trial some new material on consenting adults.

I was asked to produce a perfect impression of a patient's teeth using a new impression material. This was in the days before photoshopping and so correcting anomalies or errors in the final image was not a realistic option. Every impression I took seemed to have some flaw, often air blows that looked unsightly and not the perfect photographic image that was required for a successful marketing campaign. We then came up with a novel solution. Purchasing an icing syringe, Sheila packed the material into this, passed it to me and I syringed the contents into the patient's mouth and then placed an impression tray and prayed.

The perfect result, if not the perfect technique! And as a footnote, I used that impression material throughout my practising life, and it still proves to be very popular today.

Sheila was devoted to her golden Labrador. One morning, she was distraught. Her dog had gone missing the previous afternoon and in the evening a neighbour called to say that her dog had been knocked down by a car and had been taken to the local vet. Sheila rushed there to be told her dog was badly injured but still alive.

The next day, I was fearing the worst, but a transformed Sheila breezed into the practice, all smiles.

There was a bark outside her door that evening and, on opening it, there, right as rain, was her beloved Labrador. A case of mistaken identity (the other dog recovered).

The practice operated four days a week, and I soon adapted to this new way of life. For me, it gave the opportunity to provide high-quality care without too many time or financial constraints. It was, I soon realised, a privileged position at this relatively early stage of my career.

At the same time, I continued my association with Guy's, acting as a clinical demonstrator one day a week. This involved clinical supervision of students providing patients with restorative treatment, anything from simple fillings to more complex crowns and bridges and root treatments (often dreaded by students and patients alike). Students had to accumulate points for the treatment carried out and we also graded their work. I loved this role and also the camaraderie amongst my fellow demonstrators who were all in general practice. Unlike the full-time teaching staff at the hospital, who were often brilliant academics and specialists, I hoped we could bring practical guidance to the students from our own experiences.

Unbelievable these days but then, a group of us used to go out for a pub lunch, often to The George in Borough High Street, the only surviving coaching inn in London. We discussed the morning and sought each other's views if we had encountered difficulty with a patient, student or indeed a member of the full-time staff! And again, humour was never far away. There were some delightful characters who kept us amused with their anecdotes, some professional others not. Hedley Grabaskey, known as 'Grab', practised in St Ives in

Cambridgeshire and would travel up to Guy's every week to supervise students. A dapper man, immaculately dressed in his crisp white coat, with a charming demeanour and dry sense of humour, he was the students' favourite. There were quite frequent fogs in the area where he lived and one morning, he related how he had been out the evening before when a thick mist descended as he was driving home. He took what he thought was the correct turning heading home when he realised, to his horror, that he was on the runway of the nearby RAF base.

Just as life appeared settled, there was a dramatic change. The dental company where I was practising, which had a long history extending back over many decades, was suddenly taken over by a US-based organisation. Their headquarters in Soho was to be sold and the dental practice closed. This came as a bombshell.

Redundancy, an ever-present threat in many occupations, had never, probably naively, featured on my agenda. I recalled treating patients, themselves made redundant, and remembered the anguish they were suffering. The reality hit home. Whilst I gathered my thoughts and considered all of my options, I heard through a colleague that a children's clinic in North London was struggling and needed a dentist. I immediately applied and was accepted for the locum role.

And so started this new chapter in my life. Shoreditch was then, in the early 1980s, a depressed multi-ethnic area with high unemployment. Poverty stalked the streets. The well-equipped community dental clinic was staffed by three dentists and was exclusively for the treatment of children. An adjacent clinic provided treatment for adults.

Travelling through the City of London on the Number eight bus to the socially deprived streets of Shoreditch became a regular feature of my daily commute. Although I, like the other dentists, had a full appointment book, what became clear very soon was that on some days, I was not at all busy. Many patients did not attend their appointments for a variety of reasons, including forgetfulness, family problems, poverty or illness. I really felt that I did not earn my keep.

An enormous frustration for me was that the adjacent clinic treating adults was overwhelmed and had to turn patients away. I offered my services; after all, I was available and my surgery free, but because the funding for adult services came from a different budget, I was told very firmly that I could not help. This was my first real brush with bureaucracy. In spite of everything, I gained some valuable experience that stayed with me throughout my career. Guided by those who had much more experience than I had of treating children, I learnt much in those three months. Many were frightened and so trying to help them overcome their anxiety was as important as the treatment itself.

I remembered then the teachings of one of my tutors at Guy's. An inspirational paediatric dental consultant, she had a wonderful way with children. Confronted with an anxious or uncooperative child, Eileen Jaffe would often remark on their 'lovely shoes' and even start by polishing their fingernails, before venturing into their mouths. We may have laughed at the time, but I then understood the value of this approach.

FIVE

LEAVING GUY'S

'An Opportunity Worth Probing' were the words that leapt out at me in an advertisement in the *British Dental Journal*. Marks & Spencer were expanding the dental practice which served staff at their headquarters in Baker Street. I decided to apply, knowing that these opportunities rarely arose. The competition was likely to be intense. Several demanding interviews later, I was appointed, much to my relief. I joined a multidisciplinary team in the health services department, doctors, dentists, hygienists, chiropodists, nurses, physiotherapists and even an osteopath. The ethos was simple: to care for the health and well-being of staff by providing comprehensive, high-quality care. Staff felt valued, were happy in their work and performed better. Marks &

Spencer was regarded as the model employer and held a special place in the nation's heart. And this rubbed off on those of us who delivered the care.

Staff at all levels, from the chairman down to the most junior, were eligible for the service, and I like to think we treated them equally.

My first day didn't start off too well. I was asked to see Mr Nikolaidis who worked in the director's dining room. "Good morning, Doc," he said in his strong Greek accent as he walked into the surgery. "I have been in Akoni."

"How nice," I replied. "Is that where your home is?"

"No," he said, clearly confused. "I have been in Akoni, much pain, all night!"

It didn't take long to settle in and build relationships with patients, and we were a close-knit team. There was a certain kudos working for an organisation like Marks & Spencer, very successful and profitable and still, in those days, a paternalistic company. Marcus Sieff was chairman, a much-admired and respected figure amongst staff at all levels, strong, fair and determined. His brother, Edward, had survived an assassination attempt by Carlos the Jackal, shot in the face outside his house in St John's Wood in 1973. He was saved by his teeth, which deflected the bullet. He had been treated by my predecessor and I only saw him on one occasion.

There were many characters and personalities amongst the staff who worked there, and I loved their humour. One morning, Paul Bookbinder, a larger-than-life figure, the Company Archivist who was known for his own brand of humour, was arriving at the Marks & Spencer head office in Baker Street. He rushed into the lift, knowing he should have been at his desk by now. Standing in the lift was Lord Sieff. "Late again, Bookbinder?" he asked.

"So am I, sir," he replied.

There were some exceptional doctors and dentists. The doctors ran what was not just a private GP service for staff but were responsible for all aspects of occupational health and safety. In addition, Marks & Spencer were well known for their comprehensive health screening programmes that were offered to staff up and down the country. Free dental check-ups were also offered to staff in stores by a network of local dentists. Occasionally, I would have to go myself to carry out these examinations. On one of these occasions, I remember the sales assistant booked to see me must have been somewhat confused as to who she was seeing as she started undressing in front of me. "You can keep your clothes on whilst I examine your teeth," I exclaimed. I am not sure who was more embarrassed.

This was the late '80s and early '90s. Marks & Spencer was doing well, but changes were afoot. My role changed when I was made head of the dental service. Treatment continued to be offered to staff at the head office, and I introduced an oral cancer screening programme for staff in all stores. Fergal Nally – a Consultant in Oral Medicine at The Eastman Dental Hospital, an inspirational, softly spoken, gentle giant of a man, composer, pianist, writer and artist – was a leading expert in oral cancer who gladly offered me advice and guidance.

The screening programme, the first of its kind in the UK, was hailed as a success and gave me a certain sense of achievement.

Having set up the oral cancer screening programme, I was approached by a US pharmaceutical company to help in the evaluation of a system to detect mouth cancer earlier. The system was based on a series of three rinses which would stain potential cancers a deep blue, hence making them easier to detect than the simple visual examination with the naked eye.

Together with two colleagues, we completed a scientific evaluation to assess the acceptability of these rinses. There was much to consider, including light blue stains persisting for several hours across the lips and tongue and passing blue urine.

As a result of the study, I was invited to lecture to dentists across Europe. Wherever I went, everyone was so hospitable and welcoming. I built up a good rapport with the head of the pharmaceutical company, a delightful insightful man then well into his seventies with a wicked sense of humour. I remember he told me on one occasion how his daughter and son-in-law, who lived in San Francisco, were worried about warnings of an impending major earthquake. They decamped to Phoenix to stay with the parents until the perceived danger had passed.

In the early hours of one morning, the father and his wife, also in her seventies, got up and crept into his daughter's room where she and her husband were asleep and attached ropes to the bedstead. They then unravelled the rope and, tightening it, pulled so hard that the whole bed rocked and creaked. Their daughter awoke with a scream, thinking that the earthquake had followed them to Phoenix!

One particular lecture trip I remember well. I had been invited to Athens and had booked a taxi from my home to

Gatwick Airport. The taxi driver was Greek, a rather bizarre coincidence bearing in mind my destination. During our conversation, I explained I was going to deliver a lecture in Athens. "Do you speak Greek?" he asked. I explained that there would be dual translation. Before I left his cab, he said, "I am going to give you something to say, and the audience will love you; it is very colloquial and complimentary." He proceeded to write down phonetically a few words. "You must do it," he said, without explaining the meaning.

The morning I was due to give the lecture I was taken to the auditorium filled with hundreds of Greek dentists (there are more dentists in Athens per head of population than in most other European cities). This was daunting. I was introduced and then felt in my pocket for the slip of paper given to me by the taxi driver. A high-risk strategy, but I said the words he had told me to. I was greeted by rapturous applause and a standing ovation. To this day, I don't know what I had said!

Marks & Spencer head office staff travelled frequently to all four corners of the globe. My travel was more modest. Prior to a change of policy, I would visit towns and cities across the UK to interview and appoint local dentists to provide a screening service for Marks & Spencer staff. I would also organise training days, often inviting local specialists who made valuable contributions to delivering the screening programme. These trips were not entirely without incident.

Not only were there the usual delays on the railways: 'The train has been halted by a bovine incursion. We are awaiting the arrival of the Nuneaton fire brigade to remove a cow from the line'… 'The train has been halted as an old lady has pulled the communication cord. She is locked in the lavatory (only one of them not three of them as in the nursery rhyme). As soon as the key has been located, she will be released, and the train will be on its way'.

"'Ere, you're that geezer, aren't you?" these three young guys shouted as they pulled back the sliding door to my compartment (trains then were not all open plan).

"What geezer?" I asked.

"*Fawlty Towers*, that geezer. You're on the telly, mate, aren't you?" Maybe then, I had a vague passing resemblance to John Cleese, but I vehemently denied being him.

"No," I emphasised.

"Yes, you are; you're that geezer."

And for several minutes this dialogue continued until I said, "You mean John Cleese?"

"Yes," they said. "You are."

"No, I'm not."

"Why say it then?" There was no answer.

Hotels were selected for us. When I remarked to a patient that I would be staying in Bolton, he warned me not to make the same mistake he had. His room was on two levels. He had stripped off to take a shower and then noticed another internal door leading off his bedroom. Wondering what was behind it, he stepped through naked and into a crowded drinks party.

I did stay at that hotel, but I did not make the same mistake.

However, that evening at dinner, armed with a novel, I was perusing the menu and had acknowledged a couple on the next table. "What are you going to eat then, lad?" asked the grey-haired older man in a broad northern accent.

"I thought I would try the lamb," I said.

"Eee be careful," he said. "It's not English, it's New Zealand." Ignoring his advice, I went ahead and ordered it anyway, together with a half-bottle of Oxford Landing. "Eee, lad," he asked, "what you drinking?"

"Oxford Landing," I replied.

"Let's 'ave a look at bottle," he said, so I passed it to him. "Oxford Landing," he observed. "Bloody cheek," he said, his voice rising to a crescendo. "And it's not even English! It's bloody Australian. You can't trust anything these days." I returned to my book and felt the wine slip down a treat.

On another occasion, I was attending the British Dental Association Conference in Torquay. A series of lectures over three days, the chance to meet colleagues, exchange ideas and listen to some eminent speakers. Some lectures were always more interesting than others, and on a hot summer afternoon, I decided that the fresh sea air was a more attractive option than sitting through a long afternoon on the statistical analysis of the incidence of dental caries in non-fluoridated areas.

The sky was blue, with a few clouds on the horizon as the wind started to increase. The sea, previously calm, was starting to get a little choppy as the tide came in. The red flag was flying as I joined holidaymakers enjoying a stroll along the seafront. I became aware of a crowd gathering, looking out to sea and some pointing. I wandered over to have a closer look and saw a man, stripped to his waist, struggling to get out of the water and onto the cliffs below. This was before many people had mobile phones. Suddenly, I spotted a police car, flagged it down and explained what was happening. Within minutes, coastguards, an ambulance and more police arrived, as overhead a coastguard helicopter flew into view. As the drama before me unfolded, it occurred to me that this was far more exciting than sitting through the lecture I was supposed to be attending.

A coastguard was winched over the cliff, and he brought the hapless bather to safety, none the worse for his ordeal.

That evening, back in my hotel, I settled down to watch the TV news. The whole rescue had been filmed from the helicopter and there, in the front row of the crowd, was me. I just hope no one saw me skiving!

In 1992, I had to travel to Inverness to meet prospective dentists interested in becoming Marks & Spencer store dentists. I was given the option of staying in one of two hotels. I chose the one out of the city centre. In the morning when I awoke, I put on the TV news. The other hotel had burnt down in the night!

In the late '90s behind the scenes at the M&S head office, things were changing. In what had been a cohesive practice, cracks were beginning to appear. At around this time, the ripples of unease within the dental practice were casting a shadow over those of us who worked there and provided the care for staff.

Moves were afoot to restructure the department as part of an overall strategy to reduce costs as Marks & Spencer was going through a difficult trading time. My role would change with all the management function being passed to those with no detailed clinical knowledge nor expertise in running a dental service. Sadly, the oral cancer screening programme would cease. The writing was on the wall and for the first time, I felt a dissonance between Marks & Spencer, an organisation I had always admired and respected, and my own values.

At times during the difficult days and all the upheaval at Marks & Spencer, I would escape the politics and seek refuge at the Royal Society of Medicine (RSM). Situated in the heart of central London, the RSM is one of the country's leading providers of post-graduate education, with sections devoted to every medical and surgical speciality. For me, it provided a quiet haven to gather my thoughts and to explore my options for the future.

I had been a member there for many years and was actively involved in the section devoted to dentistry, somewhat archaically and quaintly termed the Odontology section. Soon after I left Marks & Spencer, I became president of this section and, together with my colleagues, organised scientific and clinical meetings.

One of the most fascinating days was a presentation by a highly talented medical artist called Richard Neave. Based at Manchester University, he would reconstruct faces on skulls by building up layer upon layer of clay following all the anatomical landmarks. He used his skills to help identify victims of crime or to recapture the faces of skulls found on archaeological digs. His results were remarkable. I remember asking him how he could be sure that what he produced was a realistic image of the person the skull represented. In answer, he related how a radiologist living in the Netherlands, whom he had never met nor seen, challenged him to recreate his own facial likeness on a milled model of his skull that he would send him, constructed using 3D radiographs. The only other information that was provided related to hair colour and hairline.

Richard took up the challenge and agreed to meet him with his reconstructed skull in the Netherlands to see whether his reconstruction was like the living person. The evening before they were due to meet, eating in a restaurant, Richard spotted a familiar face across the room. It was the radiologist that he had come to meet. He had managed to reconstruct a near-perfect likeness!

With all the unhappiness and uncertainty at Marks & Spencer, it was clear that I had to move on. During those months, Judy and I had had lots of discussions about the situation that was evolving. It seemed that every day more difficulties were arising and despair growing. Judy has always been a source of wise counsel, and I have always valued her opinion. She would often give me that extra push that I needed. I carefully considered all the options, and I came to the conclusion that to have my own practice in London, close to where my existing patients were, would be the best outcome. Achieving it was something else. Practices in London were expensive, my resources were limited, and I needed an income to support my family, with two daughters still at school and at crucial stages in their education.

Then, the unexpected happened. One evening I received a phone call from a dental company 'rep' whom I had known over the years. He had heard of a dentist in Harley Street, Bill Hackett, who was retiring and selling his practice.

I remember that first encounter. I walked the length of Harley Street to No.152 on the corner close to the

Marylebone Road. An imposing building with a number of doctors occupying the other rooms, his practice was on the third floor, and he greeted me as I exited the old, gated lift. We immediately hit it off. Bill Hackett, a delightful man, had practised there for around forty years, latterly single-handedly. Negotiations were hardly needed, and the purchase was agreed that same day.

He introduced me to his delightful wife Carol and his nurse Ann who agreed to stay on and work with me, ensuring continuity, which is so important. She then continued to work for me for another thirteen years before taking a well-earned retirement. He had many loyal patients and generously wrote to all of them, encouraging them to stay with the practice.

SIX

HARLEY STREET

So began this new chapter in my life at the dawn of the millennium. This was a big step for me as I was on my own for the first time in my career with a young family to support. Would the patients stay?

I felt a sense of pride when, on my first morning, I saw my name on the brass plate outside the entrance. The surgery itself had not been updated for many years and so it was a bit like stepping back in time. But it worked; I was my own boss and, most importantly, I had patients. It soon became clear that being a successful dentist was not just down to clinical expertise but business acumen. What I lacked in this field was more than compensated for by the advice generously given by my predecessor and his wife

Carol and the guidance that Judy gave me in running the practice.

Harley Street, in the heart of Marylebone, has for many years harboured the reputation of being the centre of excellence for all things medical and dental. For me, it was an eye-opener. I was somewhat unusual in that I was not a specialist like most practitioners on Harley Street but practised general dentistry. It was the variety of treatments and patients that appealed. I had always wanted patients to feel relaxed and at ease. The perception that a visit to the dentist was something to be feared, or at the least endured, was an anathema to me. Okay, a visit to the dentist was not going to be a laugh a minute but maybe it could be enjoyable.

I was blessed with such a variety of patients, many of whom had followed me from Marks & Spencer but also many who were new to me. A lot of the patients had been with the practice for many years. Their record cards, in some cases dating back to the 1930s, bore testimony in their details to their fascinating lives. It never occurred to me that the practice would have operated through the war years. What stories lay behind these record cards? I was determined to learn more.

I didn't have to wait long. Ironically, at the time I was reading a book, *Fortress Malta* by James Holland, and was gripped by the stories of heroism encapsulated within its covers. I remember reading of the exploits of one Second Lieutenant Edward Fawcett on board HMS *Bramham* escorting a convoy sailing through the Mediterranean in 1942 as part of Operation Pedestal. The convoy of merchant ships came under attack, sinking a number of ships. Edward

Fawcett launched a twenty-two-foot rowing boat and picked up over thirty survivors, and then returned to rescue more.

It then occurred to me that I had a patient Edward Fawcett who was booked to see me that very week. Could this be the same person? It seemed unlikely. This tall, upright distinguished-looking patient in his eighties arrived and introduced himself. During that first encounter, I asked him if he had ever served on HMS *Bramham*. "Yes," he replied. "How do you know?" I told him of the book I was reading. Not surprisingly he dismissed his valour with a modest wave of the arm. I learnt a few years later that his wife, also a patient, had worked at Bletchley Park and deciphered the coded message revealing the position of the German battleship *Bismarck* which allowed the Royal Navy to sink it.

Modesty was what I noticed in many of my older patients. I suppose that acts of courage and doing something memorable and vital were not as rare as they are today but even so, I could not help but be moved by the selfless modesty that I encountered.

Another patient who had been in the Wrens in the war told me she had also been at Bletchley Park but dismissed her role as if it was of no importance. For her, there was personal regret such was the secrecy surrounding code-breaking that she was never able to tell her husband what she had done. He died some thirty years after the war never knowing the secret of his wife's wartime role.

Other stories of the Second World War were revealed to me, often unexpectedly, by patients in the dental chair. One in particular made a big impression.

Harold Rose had been a patient of the practice for many years. A charming, delightful man, I knew he was a retired Professor of Finance at the London Business School and had had a distinguished career as an economist. But it was only when he was in his nineties that he told me of his time spent in Burma where he saw action on the front line.

At twenty, he was one of the youngest captains in the army. He had written an account of his time there and lent it to me to read. I found it very moving, an eyewitness account of events as they unfolded in this forgotten war that claimed numerous lives, including many of his comrades, all those years ago.

One disclosure came out of the blue. I was seeing one patient, quite a serious older lady who rarely talked much of herself and always presented a calm demeanour. Suddenly, she walked robustly into my surgery, brimming with anger, apologising for her outburst. What on earth was the matter? Sitting her down, I asked her what had happened. It transpired she had been listening to the news and had heard that an ex-intelligence officer had written a book about the activities of the secret service, breaching the accepted code of practice. She was incandescent. It turned out, as she confided in me, she had been with MI5 for all her working life. Certainly someone you wouldn't notice in a crowd and who wasn't going to sing from the rooftops about her role.

Everyone has a story. Although, with a visit to the dentist the story is usually one-sided, as carrying on a conversation with a mouthful of a variety of instruments is somewhat inhibiting. I do like chatting. It has helped over the years to relax patients, so they don't feel rushed. It helps build up a relationship which hopefully will last for many years. For me, it added another dimension to the work which I did and loved.

My life as a dentist was enriched by so many stories related to me by my patients, often about themselves or someone they loved. Some of these stories of heroic and selfless acts often go untold. Acts which, at the time, may have seemed trivial and mundane, have resonance for future generations. Often when I arrived home, I would retell these stories to my wife Judy and our daughters Clare and Abi. It became a regular feature of our evenings. They would sit there waiting for me to begin, "I had this patient today..." Some were humorous; some were sad, but it gave an insight into other people's remarkable lives that I had, for a brief moment, the privilege to listen to and share.

A delightful elderly Jewish patient came to see me. He was ninety years old and had fled Germany in the late 1930s to escape the ominous rise of the Nazis. His headmaster was a member of the Nazi Party, and with the storm clouds gathering in Europe, life was becoming increasingly perilous. After spending the duration of the war in the United States, he came to the UK. Upon arrival, he searched for the girl he had fallen in love with before the war and happily found her. Apart from a short spell as an evacuee in the Oxford countryside, she had spent the war years in London.

She later recalled her vivid memories of joining the jubilant crowds outside Buckingham Palace on VE Day and seeing the royal family come out onto the balcony eight times to the cheering crowds below. They married in the same year as the then Princess Elizabeth and Prince Philip and had become staunch royalists. He ran a successful business in London, which was a continuation of the family business that had started before the war in Germany. His original office building in Berlin still stands next to Checkpoint Charlie with the original business plaque intact, having withstood the destruction of Berlin. This somehow for me bore testimony as a powerful symbol of survival.

His wife also became a patient of mine. Her appearance belied her years: immaculately dressed, smart, sophisticated and totally unpretentious with a delightful twinkle. They were still travelling abroad widely and, on one occasion, were returning from France late at night. Her husband was driving along the M20, a journey they had done many times before. A blue flashing light appeared behind them, and they were pulled over. A policeman asked to see his driving licence. "Do you realise you were driving at 90mph?" (His age exactly.) "Perhaps it's time to consider stopping driving at your age, sir."

"Stop driving, Officer?" he replied. "How would I get to work every day?"

When I announced my retirement, his wife came to see me. "I wanted to give you a gift," she said. "And I wanted to give you something older than me," she added with her usual twinkle. I opened the gift in front of her. It was an exquisite Meissen cup and saucer which dated from 1894. I was overwhelmed by such a kind gesture.

Most of the time, dental practice, like other occupations and professions, develops its own pattern. Although the procedures and treatments may for the most part be routine, what differs every time are the individual patients. Occasionally, there comes something that breaks the pattern.

This may happen only a handful of times in general dental practice. For the most part, conditions that confront us are not life-threatening. However, as a profession we are now much more alert to the possibility that a patient may present with early signs of mouth cancer and so today, a soft tissue examination is mandatory. The patient may be completely unaware of the early signs. I remember one lady – in her sixties, a non-smoker and a low risk in terms of oral cancer – came to see me on a Friday afternoon for a routine check-up. As soon as I examined her, I realised all was not well. A large ulcer was present on the side of her tongue, which had unusual features and, from the patient's point of view, was symptomless. Late Friday afternoon with a weekend looming, she was in need of urgent treatment. Fortunately, after a series of phone calls, she was seen that afternoon and treatment began soon after. A few years later, she was clear of the cancer.

A guardsman fracture, as its name suggests, describes a peculiar type of injury related to guardsmen. Spending long periods on parade in searing heat and wearing a bearskin, a guardsman may succumb to a simple faint. What complicates this minor episode is that a guardsman may faint to attention (such is their discipline) and land on his chin, causing a bilateral fracture of the condyles (the part of the lower jaw that articulates with the skull). I had, unsurprisingly, no guardsmen amongst my patients and so it was extremely unlikely I would ever encounter this type of fracture. However, one afternoon, a scaffolder working on the outside of my building was manoeuvring scaffolding poles into a lift when the door was closed, forcing one of the poles in an upwards movement, striking the hapless scaffolder on the chin. The injury mimicked that of a guardsman on parade, a fracture of his condyles. Having assessed him, I referred him to hospital. This episode just underlines what I had learnt in years of practice – be prepared for the unexpected.

Dentists frequently encounter patients with broken teeth, and this is one of the most common problems that we are asked to treat. Fractured teeth often occur as the result of trauma, sometimes a sporting accident, falls, especially in children, or as a consequence of extensive tooth decay.

So, the call I received from a patient complaining of a fractured front tooth was not unusual but the circumstances, as I was to discover, were quite remarkable. The patient, a male in his forties and an experienced scuba diver, walked into my surgery covered in bandages. A fractured tooth seemed to be the least of his worries.

He explained that he had been diving off the coast of Indonesia when he encountered a salt-water crocodile that attacked him; that in itself was unusual in the waters where he was diving. His 'dive buddy' was unable to help him. The crocodile lacerated his arm and pulled his mask off, fracturing his front tooth in the process. Eventually showing great presence of mind, he stuck his fingers into the crocodile's eyes and got away. He survived the ordeal and spent several weeks recovering in hospital. I repaired his tooth and he returned to diving undaunted by his near-disastrous experience.

Sometimes things happen closer to home. Every morning, I was greeted by the commissionaire, Len, who operated the antiquated gated lift that must have been installed when the building was constructed early in the 20th century.

One day, he came up to me with raging toothache. He wasn't a patient of mine but, of course, I had to see him. I sat him down and needed to complete a record card. I couldn't remember his surname, and as I saw him every morning, I was embarrassed to ask. "Len," I asked, "how do you spell your surname?"

"Usual way," he said. "S-M-I-T-H."

Always listen to patients is a lesson I learnt very early on in my career and is a fundamental requirement of dental and indeed medical practice.

By contrast, there are also some Never rules that I have learnt over the years.

Never ask a patient 'how was it for you?' after root canal treatment (delving into their root canals). Never say 'you will only feel a small prick'. Never assume patients understand about taking tablets. I prescribed some co-codamol effervescent tablets for a female patient as pain relief. The tablets, about the size of a 10p piece, have to be dissolved in water and swallowed. She then related to me the experience of her husband the previous summer whilst on holiday in France. Unwell, he had gone to a local doctor and was prescribed the same tablets for pain relief. On returning to where he was staying, he went to the bathroom to take them. He emerged some thirty minutes later pale and sweating. "Whatever's the matter?" asked his concerned wife.

"I just can't get these tablets up," he said.

"What do you mean?" his wife asked. "Up where?"

"Up my bottom," he said. It suddenly dawned on her that because they were in France, her husband had assumed all medication was given as suppositories.

She didn't make the same mistake!

On another occasion, a new patient came to see me. She was French and this was her first visit to a British dentist. I had always used the traditional pink thymol mouthwash tablets that dissolve in water. Sitting in the chair, the patient saw the tablet fizzing in the water. "Oh," she said in a strong French accent, "'ow kind… I 'ave never been given pain killers before my appointment. *Très gentil*."

When taking a medical history from one of my more eccentric patients, she told me she was taking Valium. "Why has your doctor prescribed them?" I asked.

"He hasn't," she replied. "The vet prescribed them for my dog."

Never assume patients know where to sit when entering the surgery. Anxious and in unfamiliar surroundings, I have known patients to sit on the dentist's or nurse's stool rather than the patient's chair. Not wishing to cause embarrassment, I would simply say, "I think you would be more comfortable here."

Never leave patients alone in the surgery. I made the mistake once. I was treating an adult male patient who was on the autistic spectrum and his mother, a rather obese lady, was with him. My nurse was dealing with another patient on the phone when I was called to deal with a query. Excusing myself, I left the patient with his mother. Moments later, there was an enormous crash from the surgery. I rushed in to see the mother legs akimbo on the floor, the dentist's stool upside down and the patient laughing uproariously.

Much to her embarrassment, the mother confessed she wanted to play dentist and decided to see what it would be like!

This scenario reminded me of the well-known TV sketch by Rowan Atkinson who plays a hapless patient left alone in a dentist's surgery trying to decipher his X-rays and drill his own teeth. Fortunately, it didn't get that far.

During my time in practice, I must have seen patients from virtually all professions and occupations, none more varied than the patients I saw in Harley Street. The impression of those visiting Harley Street is that they are wealthy and come from a narrow, privileged background. This was certainly not my experience.

Occasionally, patients could be difficult and demanding, but often this was for good reason. Anxiety and stress could trigger unreasonable demands, but only a few patients were naturally difficult, the 'Mrs Buzzys' of my father-in-law's day. Weekends presented a particular challenge for me, and I always had out-of-hours calls transferred to my mobile. Very few patients abused this and only one 'Mrs Buzzy' would call frequently at weekends and sometimes late at night.

However, one Saturday afternoon, a call caught me completely off-guard. My mobile went and the caller, claiming to be from the Metropolitan Police, said a call had been received from a mother that her child was locked in the toilet in my basement. I assumed this was a scam call and told the caller that I had no basement and certainly no child locked in the toilet as I was at home with my family. Making clear I was fed up with scam calls, I asked for the 'police officer's' name, rank and number; astounded, he gave them to me! It was a genuine call. A child had been locked in the building where my practice was, and I was the only contact number the police could trace. It transpired that the child had been seen that morning by a child therapist who, after the appointment, had left, not realising the child was still there when the building was locked. I gave the police the contact details for the landlord, and all was well. The child was released none the worse for their unexpected incarceration. When I realised that the call had been genuine, I apologised for not believing the caller. "You can never be too careful, sir," was the police officer's generous reply.

I never cease to be surprised, indeed on occasions astounded, even after many years of practice, by the encounters I had in the dental chair. All of them interesting but for different reasons. Some amusing, some sad and emotional, many uplifting and a few, well, concerning.

Often, there was a lighter note. One new patient was a London cabbie whose wife had been a patient for some time. Her husband had not been to a dentist for many years and had broken a front tooth. "Will I have an injection?" he asked.

"Yes, if you would like one."

"Do you use cocaine?" he asked.

"No," I said. "Not cocaine, something similar."

"What's it called?" he said.

"There are a number of local anaesthetics, for example Lignocaine."

"Anything else?" he asked.

"Yes," I said. "Articaine, Prilocaine."

"Any others?"

"Mepivacaine," I said.

"I've got another one for you," he said. "Michael Caine, and not a lot of people know that!"

A retired solicitor immaculately dressed with a spotted

bow tie and distinctive glasses had broken an upper right molar tooth. I gave him a local anaesthetic and placed a filling and he left happy but numb.

That evening, I noticed as I left the practice a glasses lens lying on the stairs. I picked it up in case someone claimed it the next day. And they did. The next morning, the retired solicitor's wife called the practice. "I don't suppose you've found a glasses lens?" she asked. I told her that I had. She related how her husband had left the practice and had great difficulty focusing. He couldn't see the number of his bus and he tried unsuccessfully to do the crossword on the way home.

"I don't know what the dentist has done," he said to his wife when he got home, "but since I had an injection, I can't see out of my right eye."

"You bloody fool," she said. "Your lens is missing."

One of my nurses who had worked with me at Marks & Spencer followed me to Harley Street. Tough, no-nonsense with a Welsh mother and a Jamaican father, Pauline was intensely loyal and would always stand up for herself.

Meeting my patients for the first time, I had learnt to expect the unexpected. Nothing, however, had prepared me, or more accurately, Pauline, for one particular encounter. An eighty-year-old diminutive gentleman (an inappropriate description as it happens) walked into my surgery. I introduced myself. He looked at me and said in a broad Northern accent, "I am the most successful litigious solicitor in London," presumably intended as a warning shot. He required new dentures, a process that involves several visits for impression taking and all the measurements required to achieve a successful outcome.

Following the first set of impressions, he needed to return for another appointment. He asked for it to be on a date when Pauline would be present. I took this as a compliment to her obvious nursing skills. But at the second appointment, his true motives became clear.

Pauline accompanied him in the lift down to reception where his daughter was waiting. During that short descent, he attempted to fondle her – his advances were firmly rebutted. She wouldn't let me speak to him as she believed that this would compromise his ongoing treatment. I agreed reluctantly but made sure his appointments were on days when another nurse would be with me.

He didn't get the message. He started by sending her love poems and a Valentine's card. Next came pornographic pictures. I contacted my defence organisation for guidance. Their advice was clear: complete his treatment, allow no contact with the nurse, but take no other action. They said it seemed that he was just a 'sad old man'. I suspect that the advice would be different today.

I sent him his final account for treatment. He sent me a cheque and wrote me a letter, which I still have, explaining that he had deducted from my fees his fee for his hourly rate whilst he was attending my practice!

It occurred to me that mine might have been a rather peculiar practice. I think, however, all practices have patients with their own peculiarities and experience peculiar occurrences from time to time. It is simply a snapshot of life encapsulated within the walls of a dental practice, but with me, it left a lasting impression.

As did a visit to my practice in 2004. Tony Blair was

prime minister and there were moves internationally to build better relations between the West and Colonel Gaddafi's regime in Libya. This was hardly at the forefront of my mind when, one afternoon, the receptionist called me to say there was a lady asking to see me. I wasn't expecting a patient as it was lunchtime, and I assumed it must be a representative from a dental company. They would often pop in on the off-chance in order to promote their particular products. I said I would see her.

A smartly dressed young woman introduced herself by saying she worked for a government agency who were assisting with the political process aimed at reintegrating Libya into the international community and to help shed its image of a pariah state. I was puzzled until she produced a folder containing the dental records of a patient. She explained that the patient was in need of dental treatment in Libya and was a person of some importance. She offered to fly me out to provide the treatment for her. It transpired that the patient was one of Colonel Gaddafi's wives.

My bewilderment grew. Why was I being asked? Had anyone else been approached? I felt uneasy. It was clear I was viewing the confidential records of a patient with no evidence of their consent. I called my defence organisation. Their advice was unequivocal. With much relief, I declined. I heard no more, leaving me with more questions than answers.

From time to time, patients were referred to me from The Eastman Dental Hospital for follow-up routine treatment.

One patient left a deep impression. A larger-than-life Italian lady breezed into my surgery rather like a tornado. Brimming with warmth and a temperament both exhausting and exhilarating, she never failed to brighten the dullest of days. She would rarely come alone and always bearing gifts of champagne and smoked salmon. Most often, she would be accompanied by her husband and daughter. I am sure that they would sometimes forget where they were and would inject an impression of Italian family life into my Harley Street surgery. It was wonderful! But what was more astounding was her life story, which unfolded as if thumbing through the pages of a romantic novel.

Her husband was many years younger than her. It transpired that they both came from the same small village in Italy where an earthquake struck. The patient, then a girl in her teens, pulled a baby from the rubble of the village that was all but destroyed.

Many years later, working at the reservations desk for Alitalia, she was checking in one of the passengers when she recalled the name. It was the baby she had rescued all those years before.

A chance encounter and in spite of the years between them, they fell in love. They were married and had a delightful daughter who also became a patient of mine.

That was the story she told to me and one I wish to believe and retell. It is a testimony to the best of the human spirit.

Some situations which wouldn't ordinarily lend themselves to humour can suddenly become funny, often when you least expect it. Then, there are the feelings of guilt that perhaps this is laughter at someone else's misfortune.

Mr Macarthy, a patient of the practice for many years, did, however, see the funny side of his experience when he explained to me when he arrived for his appointment why he was bruised, battered and bandaged around his face and arms.

He had landed at Heathrow Airport the previous evening and had attempted to retrieve his suitcase from the luggage carousel but, being of slim build and short, was pulled onto the conveyor belt and carried round full circle until retrieved by other passengers also waiting for their luggage.

I was often amused by patients relating tales of their own. Christopher Drury, retired and an erstwhile competitor in the London Marathon, was a great raconteur and never missed an opportunity to tell a story, sometimes a long one.

He had been in hospital to have an orthopaedic procedure under general anaesthetic. The anaesthetist visited him for his preoperative assessment. "What do you do?" he asked. He started to tell him at length, looked up to see why he had got no response, only to discover that the anaesthetist had fallen asleep. An unusual case of role reversal.

From time to time, I was contacted by medical colleagues also in Harley Street and asked to see a patient for dental advice.

One such patient who was referred to me was visiting from Africa. Resplendent in colourful traditional dress, this tall, charismatic gentleman in his eighties arrived at my surgery. He was not alone. He was accompanied by a fellow countryman (not in traditional dress) who introduced himself as his personal physician. Although the patient's name did not mean anything to me, it was clear he must be someone of considerable importance and influence. He was charming and his treatment was straightforward. His physician stayed with him throughout and, on leaving, settled his account, insisting on paying more than was requested. After he had left, I 'googled' his name. He was chairman of a national political party in his country, very active in politics and had clearly worked hard to raise living standards. However, one line left me thinking: 'If you want anything done, or anyone killed, he's your man'.

Having spent some forty years in practice and seen patients of every age, background, race and sexuality, I could still be surprised. On one occasion, a patient of mine asked if I would see his daughter who was in some pain with a troublesome wisdom tooth.

As soon as she entered the surgery, she told me she was very nervous and had a needle phobia. I reassured her but could not fail to notice the multiple piercings in her nose, ears and, more importantly, tongue.

I sat her in the chair and started to examine her mouth. Pulling back her lower lip, I was confronted with a tattoo, written so it was the correct way up for me to easily read it. Two words: 'fuck off'. Later, I heard similar from a nurse who was working on a gynae unit. A patient who was being examined had dyed her pubic hair green. Above this was a tattoo with a clear message: 'Keep off the Grass'.

There were no shortages of surprises. An elderly gentleman came to see me for the first time. He was eighty-seven years old and had been a GP all his working life. "When did you retire?" I asked him.

"Retire?" he answered. "I haven't retired."

A few months later, I had to extract a molar tooth for him. The procedure was straightforward, but I always telephoned patients the next day to check that they were okay. When I telephoned, his wife answered, and I asked to speak to her husband to see how he was. "He's out on a house call," she remarked, as if it was the most normal thing in the world.

As a dentist, one of the most difficult diagnostic dilemmas is determining the cause of facial pain. Even with toothache itself, identifying the particular tooth causing the symptoms can take time and various investigations. Severe facial pain can sometimes be debilitating and mimic more serious medical conditions.

One patient in his eighties, whom I had known for many years, was booked in to see me for repair to a fractured molar tooth. His wife called that same morning to cancel the appointment as her husband had developed severe facial pain in the night and was attended by three paramedics and blue-lighted to hospital.

Tests were carried out and a diagnosis of trigeminal neuralgia was made. He was discharged on powerful medication and told he would be admitted for surgery the following week as this would be the best option to alleviate his symptoms. He was anxious that his tooth should be restored prior to his admission and came to see me.

Having taken a detailed history, I examined him. I noted that he had a fractured upper right molar and that the facial pain, which was continuing despite the medication, was radiating over the right side of his face. I investigated the tooth; he had a very inflamed pulp (nerve tissue). This, I believed, was the likely cause of his symptoms and referred him to a maxillofacial colleague who confirmed the findings and extracted the troublesome tooth, saving him from undergoing a potentially major surgical procedure. A sigh of relief all round.

Does history repeat itself? I wondered that when a new patient came to see me. As he sat in my chair, a story both unexpected and shocking unfolded but left me with the distinct impression that I had heard a similar tale before. An Iranian by birth (with joint Canadian nationality), a journalist, he had been covering the Iranian elections in 2009 for *Newsweek* when, staying with his elderly mother in Tehran, he was suddenly arrested, suspected of being a CIA spy, and incarcerated for four months, blindfolded and subjected to beatings and psychological torture. He was eventually released after a global campaign supported by Hillary Clinton. He wrote of his experiences in his book *Then They Came for Me* published in 2012.

Why did this sound familiar? It was forty years earlier, as I was embarking on my dental career, that a friend, whom I had met when I was training in hospital management, had some shocking news of his own. His father John Coleman, whom I had met briefly when he was a medical missionary in Bethnal Green, travelled to Iran in 1977 where he and his wife took charge of a clinic in Yadz. Then came the news of their capture and, together, they were held captive for two hundred days until their release was negotiated by Terry Waites, the Archbishop of Canterbury's envoy. His faith sustained him.

I guess I am inquisitive by nature, my family would say nosey. Over the years in practice, my life has been enriched by hearing the stories of others, often triggered in a most unexpected way.

One such story was of a patient who had been coming to the practice for years. I was glancing through her records and noticed that her name before marriage was that of an old English aristocratic family. I asked her if she was related. "Oh no," she exclaimed. "My father Herbert Grunwald was a Jewish refugee from Nazi Germany and had changed his name to Herbert de Gray after the war." An amazing story then unfolded. In 1934, her father had been working as a photo reporter in Austria and was interviewing the then Austrian Chancellor when two Nazis dressed as soldiers stormed into his office and assassinated the Chancellor, all recorded on his film. He managed to make his escape from the Chancellor's office, and his pictures appeared across the world. It was part of an attempted coup by the Austrian Nazi party.

Four years later, when Hitler did march into Austria, her father was visited by the Gestapo, attracted by his notoriety. They seized his passport. Realising he was in imminent danger of arrest, he managed, after a turbulent journey and suffering from acute appendicitis, to flee via Italy and Paris to England. Most of his family perished in the Holocaust. On arrival in England, he joined the Pioneer Corps of the British Army. For a long time after his experiences, he slept with a revolver under his pillow.

It was many years later that his daughter was reunited with long-lost family members, by then scattered across all four corners of the globe. This story shows the strength of the human spirit in overcoming the odds and demonstrates the triumph of freedom over repression.

The practice I took over at the beginning of the millennium had been established some one hundred years before and I was only the fifth dentist to have run the practice. Some of the patients remembered going there for treatment as children in the war years; others, as young adults, recalled the night-time blackouts and often deserted streets and walking long distances to get there, the disruption, devastation and ever-present fear of bombing raids. One in particular remembered cowering terrified under the dining table with her mother during an air raid. Such emotions were a distant memory.

Then, half a century later came 9/11, the events on that day etched in the memory of all of us who heard the devastating news as it unfolded of the attack on the twin towers in New York. Many, like myself, listened or watched with incredulity as the horrific attacks were streamed live.

That afternoon, patients, myself and my nurse said little and listened in stunned silence to the reports on the radio. Travelling home that evening, I saw the fear and anxiety clearly visible on the faces of my fellow commuters.

Then, four years later came the London bombings on the bus and tube network. Initially, the news was of a series of explosions caused by power surges, but soon it was clear there had been multiple bombings. The streets outside my practice in Marylebone were filled with the sounds of sirens. Public transport was suspended across London. That evening, I joined hundreds of others walking across London, anxious, worried and uncertain. And later, I heard from patients with their own stories to tell who had been in the midst of the attacks and others, Muslims, who had been shunned and treated with suspicion. Those emotions and fears were perhaps faintly reminiscent of what the previous generation had suffered day after day during the Second World War.

Over the forty years that I practised, I was privileged to have a succession of wonderful nurses to assist me. Some I have already mentioned. They were loyal, compassionate, competent and hard-working. In Harley Street, I always had two nurses who shared the role. Debbie had worked with me at Marks & Spencer and I was fortunate that she joined me later in Harley Street. The care she showed patients with her empathy and understanding helped to calm even those who were most anxious.

A dental nurse needs a great breadth of knowledge, practical ability, patience and a caring personality. Ideally, a strong partnership and bond develops between dentist and nurse. A good nurse will often anticipate the requirements of the dentist even before the dentist is aware of them. Frequently, a particular instrument would be handed to me before I had even asked for it and, on occasions, before I even knew I needed it. I have much to thank my nurses for.

Susanna was a nurse who guided me through my early days in Harley Street. Finnish with a South London Finnish accent, she had a no-nonsense, uncompromising attitude to life and spoke it as it was. Never complaining, she was such a stoic, positive person who, when diagnosed in her early forties with breast cancer, never faltered in her positive outlook and remained full of life and vigour. Throughout her treatment, she refused to take more than a few days off until one day, she fell asleep in the practice. Years later, patients would ask after her, such was the impression she made.

I needed to recruit a new nurse urgently. After contacting an agency, a nurse walked through my door. Leazel had arrived in this country from South Africa. She had had a challenging upbringing and remained close to her grandmother in South Africa. Her family had been impacted by the effects of crime and violence and this was a great burden for her to carry. Life since her arrival in the UK had also been tough, but she was determined to succeed. She had great ambition. Working for me on a part-time basis over several years, she was popular with patients with her disarming personality and sense of humour which was infectious. In many ways, I felt a fatherly responsibility for her living so far away from her family with no connections in the UK.

In recent years in practice, dental nurses needed to be properly trained and registered, like dentists, with the General Dental Council. This was an important step in ensuring high standards throughout the profession and was a sensible use of regulation, unlike some other examples.

Prior to this, dental nurses could sit a national examination and for several years, I was an examiner. Standards were high, with the emphasis on clinical and practical skills. Although in addition to the practical tests and vivas, there was a written paper, a candidate would not be failed if their answers were grammatically wrong. The correct or incorrect use of the English language was of lesser importance to my mind than having competent clinical and practical abilities. Which is why, when a candidate in answering a question on how to teach an adolescent to maintain good oral health wrote 'genital brushing', I did not fail her.

SEVEN

AN INSPECTOR CALLS

There was a knock on the door of my practice in Harley Street. "I'm an inspector with the Care Quality Commission (CQC)," the lady remarked. "I have some questions for you." I invited her in. "How many beds have you got?" she asked.

"Beds?" I queried. "None. This is a dental practice."

"Sorry," she said. "Yesterday I inspected a care home so forgive the confusion."

That conversation did not happen but it could so easily have done due to the confusion that accompanied the introduction of CQC checks on dental practices, which at the time was viewed by many as yet another layer of regulation and bureaucracy.

This was one of the most notable changes for me during my practising career. Many of us had observed across all walks of life that the volume of red tape and bureaucracy was a scourge of the late 20th and early part of the 21st centuries. In dentistry and in medicine it began to have a significant impact on patient care. Sometimes the effects were positive, ensuring high standards, but there was also a negative impact that caused concerns.

In 2009, the then Labour government set up the CQC to regulate all health and social care in England and Wales. In dental practice, the NHS had regulated standards and provision of care, but there was little regulation for practices operating in the private sector. True, dentists needed to be registered with the General Dental Council, who were charged with upholding standards and ensuring dentists had the necessary skills to deliver care to patients, but the practices themselves were unregulated.

Although many would not argue about the need for regulation, few in the profession had envisaged the way such regulation would be introduced and implemented. In 2011, all dental practices in England and Wales had to be registered with the CQC. This process was onerous and involved many stages. Rather than have different criteria for different sectors of health and social care, a 'one size fits all' approach was applied across all sectors, including dental practices, one suspects for reasons of speed of implementation and cost limitation. Dental practices had to adhere to multiple outcomes in order to be compliant and be able to deliver care for their patients. Among these criteria, two stood out: ensuring that patients did not suffer from malnutrition nor dehydration during their appointments in the practice. Appropriate for care homes but hardly applicable to dental practices where appointments are often less than an hour in length!

With mounting frustration and concern, many in the profession, including the British Dental Association, attempted to exert influence to change the criteria and adopt a more focused and appropriate approach. I wrote to David Cameron, the then prime minister. Most of these pleas for a sensible, rational approach fell on deaf ears. I enlisted the help of my local MP, and I was grateful for his support. What struck me was that the decision-makers were completely out of touch with reality. They often paid lip service when listening to these concerns but, in truth, had no real understanding of the proposals nor intention to change the focus of this new regulation. This was summed up for me in the correspondence I had from those at the Department of Health who were responsible for dental services. Clearly, their intention was to proceed with this new regulation and ride rough shod over the dissenting views of the profession. This reinforced the view of many people that politicians often do not have a grasp of the real issues that affect people, even those in the areas that they have responsibility for.

Once my dental practice was registered, I underwent an inspection to ensure all the relevant regulations were being met. This process confirmed, in my opinion, that things had to change. The inspection was carried out by an inspector who, although legally trained, had absolutely no idea of dental practice. She had previously inspected a care home and her knowledge of any clinical aspects was rudimentary to say the least.

Certificates were checked, policies reviewed, systems examined, but it was simply a 'tick box' exercise that clearly would not ensure that practices were providing a safe, caring environment for their patients.

Even the term 'patient' had been questioned. Some years earlier, an NHS Trust ordered staff not to refer to people receiving medical care as patients but as clients.

This not only demonstrated a misunderstanding of our roles but also devalued both practitioners and those that we care for. Patients are those receiving care, who are given time, are listened to and treated with sympathy, understanding and expertise. There is something special about the term patient, and although to give a precise definition is difficult, it is well understood by those who deliver the care.

Eventually, the profession was listened to and change did happen. The CQC acknowledged that when they first started regulating dentists, the organisation did not get the model right. There was an acceptance that inspections of dental practices should be focused and not be reliant solely on unqualified inspectors. A partnership between the lay inspectors (who had necessary but different skills) and Specialist Advisors (clinically qualified) was proposed, and these new style inspections introduced. I was invited to apply to become one of these advisors and, following a selection process, was appointed. I felt a little like a poacher turned gamekeeper, but I did feel I could make a small contribution in helping to ensure that practices were providing safe care for their patients.

After several years as a Specialist Advisor (a role I continued when I retired from practice), the overall impression is that most dental practices, both NHS and private, are providing a high standard of care. I saw many, many examples of practices going the extra mile in ensuring the patients were treated with care and compassion, often in very difficult circumstances.

In spite of all the seriousness surrounding regulation, or maybe because of it, humour remained a vital part of my practice. One of my patients, David Taylor, a very talented artist from Seaford in East Sussex, also sketched cartoons. Inspired by the eccentric thoughts that he had while sitting in my chair, he would often send me cartoons after his visits depicting his thoughts at the time. Some were in the style of Heath Robinson, illustrating some whimsical elaborate machines for delivering dental treatment; others were in the style of Donald McGill who, in the 1940s, was well known for his saucy seaside postcards. I displayed these on the walls of the surgery (the risqué ones high up!), together with others that I had acquired from the brilliant *Daily Telegraph* cartoonist, Matt. He went through a phase of producing cartoons with a dental theme which were published in the *Telegraph*. I loved them and so did my patients, who would often loiter, viewing them rather than rushing out of the surgery once the treatment was finished. These cartoons, together with pictures painted for me by other patients, really helped create a relaxed environment for patients and for me. Humour makes a good distraction technique, and these cartoons were a tangible example of how successful such a technique could be.

In the background, I would play Classic FM, which again seemed to relax my patients.

On one occasion, one of my more elderly patients, a widower, was sitting in my chair having just completed his treatment. On the radio, a piece of music was playing that he immediately recognised as a piece his late wife, a professional viola player, used to play. He was entranced. "May I please listen for a little longer as I would love to know who is playing this piece?"

"Of course," I said.

"You've no one waiting, have you?" I had, but I hadn't the heart to tell him. It was a long piece and lasted for another ten to fifteen minutes or so. We then waited for the end, and the announcement of who was playing the viola, in silence.

EIGHT

RETIREMENT BECKONS

After forty years of practising, my thoughts turned to retirement. When patients had asked me, I usually said I had no firm plans to retire, which was true. I loved my work and the interaction I had with patients, the variety and the challenges. No two days were ever the same. On the other hand, there was much more we as a family wanted to do. Clare and Abi had some years before both graduated from their universities and the ceremonies at Bristol and Durham had brought back memories of my own graduation all those years ago and filled me with a sense of pride in their achievements. I felt I had been very privileged to have had such a fulfilling career and met so many interesting people, but I felt the time was approaching when I would finally put down my mirror and probe and hang up my drill. But my interest in and enthusiasm for dentistry would never waiver. I hope, looking back, that I managed to make a small contribution to breaking the taboo of dentistry and to show that a visit to the dentist, although not everyone's idea of fun, could nonetheless be enjoyable and enriched by the humour that pervades our lives. Also as important, I didn't want to let my patients down, many of whom I regarded as friends who went back many years. I wanted to make sure that when I did retire, the practice was in safe hands.

I wrote personally to all my patients explaining my decision to retire. In the final weeks before I retired, I was overwhelmed by the generosity of my patients. Never had I expected to receive so many cards, letters, emails and gifts. I was lost for words.

On my last day, I packed up the items that were special to me. The cartoons and pictures that had adorned my walls and an old treadle drill (rather like a Singer sewing machine) that had been in use over a hundred years previously. Its most recent outing had been in the 1970s when my predecessor had used it by candlelight during the power cuts caused by the miners' strike.

I started to look back over my long career in dentistry, the variety and the people I had met over the years, patients and colleagues. It is vital in practice, particularly in a single-handed practice like mine, that you have a network of colleagues to help and support you. Colleagues often with different skills to whom to refer patients and speak to for advice.

One of my most valued colleagues was Roger Davies, a medically qualified oral surgeon who specialised in treating patients with special needs. Together on a regular basis, we treated patients who were medically compromised (with a range of health conditions), giving them the opportunity to be seen in my practice rather than in hospital.

It was an arrangement that worked extremely well and was very rewarding. Roger provided a level of care and compassion for these patients which they and I were grateful for. There was another dimension to these sessions. Many of these patients had endured much in their lives and their stories were often inspirational in the way they had coped with their experiences. Roger was a great listener and also raconteur, and we both chipped in with our own comments. Consequently, these appointments proved to be enjoyable for all of us.

Much of the treatment I provided could only have been achieved with the assistance of dental technicians who made the dentures, crowns and bridges and veneers for patients. I worked closely with two highly skilled technicians who had laboratories in the West End, each of them specialising in their respective fields.

John was a prosthetics technician who constructed for my patients full and partial dentures and, with an ageing patient population, there was a significant need for his expertise.

Richard specialised in dental ceramics – crowns, bridges and veneers – and was a tremendous help to me, particularly when treating the more complex cases where facial aesthetics were so important. Because both technicians worked close by, they would often come and see the patients to discuss their requirements. They helped me achieve far more for my patients than I could have done on my own and their advice in tricky situations was a great support to both myself and my patients.

I had many colleagues and friends in the profession to whom I owe a debt of gratitude. I hope in some way I returned the favours. I have had such a varied career and, looking back, it had evolved in a way I could not have envisaged nor planned better.

There were moments, of course, as with any career, when doubts seeped into my mind as to whether I was heading in the right direction. Again, this was where Judy was always there encouraging me, with a strong voice and more confidence in me than I had at times in myself.

Over so many years and in many different places, I saw thousands of patients, all with different needs and expectations. I hope that I treated them all with the same level of care and compassion. There were complex cases, others straightforward, and no two patients were ever the same. Was I always happy with the treatment I provided? Of course not, but I always tried my best. Inevitably, there were occasions when things didn't go according to plan and, with the benefit of hindsight, I would have done things differently. Mistakes can happen, but unlike other medical and surgical specialties, mistakes in dentistry, although serious, rarely have devastating consequences.

I did lose sleep over some patients, agonising over their treatments. Many patients are on complex drug regimes, and all this needs to be accounted for when delivering treatment. Mistakes do happen and the consequences can be dire. I remember one particular patient whom I had known for thirty years. She presented with a dental abscess and the treatment, which was straightforward, required extraction of the offending tooth. What was not straightforward and was totally unexpected was the failure of the mouth to heal. A condition called a dry socket is a relatively common occurrence after an extraction. It is painful, lasts a few days, but always responds to simple measures. This did not. This was not a dry socket but a condition far more serious called medicine-related osteochemonecrosis of the jaw, where the bone around the extraction socket dies. It is a recognised and rare complication of an extraction in patients who are on anti-resorptive bone medication. On this occasion, a thorough medical history failed to elicit that this patient was on this type of drug and, upon referral to hospital, again her drug regime was missed. It is something I have encountered over the years where, understandably, some patients fail to make the connection between medication prescribed by their doctor and the dental treatment they are undergoing. This underlines the need for doctors and dentists to liaise closely to ensure patients have all the necessary information, particularly as drug regimes become ever more complex. Fortunately, this patient made a full recovery.

Sometimes, however, there is too much information. I shared the reception and waiting room with other practitioners, which is common practice in the West End of London.

One particular new female patient came to see me. She was in her fifties, and I sat her down to begin the consultation. I could see she felt uneasy. I asked her if everything was alright. "Why," she asked, "if I have come to see you about a broken tooth, do you need to know all about my sexual habits?" I was somewhat taken aback. A new temporary receptionist had given her the wrong medical questionnaire – one destined for the sexual health clinic!

A medical colleague, a patient, related a story of his own. On joining a new practice, he decided to review his patients' records and their prescriptions. He came across what he thought must be an anomaly. A female patient aged eighty-one had a repeat prescription for the contraceptive pill. He arranged to see her. "I've been reviewing your medication," he said, "and I see you are prescribed the contraceptive pill. This isn't necessary for someone of your age."

"Oh, yes it is, Doctor," she said. "It helps me to sleep."

"Contraceptive pills don't act as a sedative; they don't aid your sleeping."

"Oh, yes it does, Doctor," she said. "Every morning at breakfast, I crush it into my sixteen-year-old granddaughter's orange juice, then I know I will sleep well that night!"

'Tales of the Unexpected' sum up a few incidents that I encountered over the years which were beyond the scope of dental practice. All of us, from time to time, are asked to do something beyond our comfort zone and this happens in all walks of life.

As dentists, we are regularly trained in the treatment of medical emergencies, hoping these skills will not be required. Fortunately, medical emergencies in general dental practice are relatively uncommon. But medical emergencies can occur anywhere.

Travelling home one evening in the rush hour, only a few years since I had qualified, I found myself well beyond my usual sphere of practice. On a crowded commuter train at Clapham Junction railway station, a male passenger had collapsed and was still sitting upright in his seat. He was apparently lifeless. Having laid him flat, I started CPR in a completely surreal scenario. No one else seemed to move, and when the paramedics arrived, they took over. Later, I called the hospital. He had not survived. That evening, I shed tears for a man I hadn't known.

I always used to arrive at my practice early and was usually first in the building. One particular morning, with my nurse Pauline, we were organising our day when there was a frantic knocking on my surgery door. A distraught man was shouting that his wife, who was over forty weeks pregnant, had collapsed on the stairway. Together with Pauline (who never seemed to be phased by any unexpected occurrence), we administered oxygen until paramedics swiftly came to our aid.

The patient was rapidly transported to hospital and her baby delivered – a lucky escape all round!

Flying to Sardinia one summer with the family, I noticed, an hour or so into the flight, that a passenger a few rows in front of me had adopted a strange position. He was bent double over the armrest, his head dangling above the aisle. He was clearly unconscious. I quickly pressed the call button and went to help him. A steward and a nurse on board came to assist. We placed him on the floor, gave him oxygen and he slowly recovered. He had suffered what appeared to be a vasovagal attack, a simple faint.

Then, the unexpected happened. The captain asked whether I thought the plane should be turned around! It was not my decision to make, but as we were virtually halfway to our destination and the passenger had recovered, I am pleased that we continued on our way. When we landed, the plane was met by an ambulance, and he was wheeled off by paramedics. We saw him later, none the worse for his experience, which was put down to overindulgence and no sleep at a friend's wedding, together with an early morning flight.

I was given a free cup of tea for my help. I remember my brother-in-law, a doctor, who assisted with a medical emergency on a BA flight, was given a bottle of champagne. I guess that's the difference with a budget airline!

I began to think about the various traits of human nature that I had encountered in my patients. The kindness, generosity, the selflessness and the modesty of many, most, it seemed, underlined by that very human quality of humour. Admittedly, I met a few who displayed arrogance and vanity and some who were consumed by their own self-interest. I came across only a very few who were clearly dishonest and even fewer who failed to pay their accounts and only one who gave a false address. I took very little cash, but there is one occasion I remember well. An elderly Greek gentleman came to see me. He had pedalled his bike up a very busy Harley Street in the wrong direction against the oncoming traffic. His treatment completed, he said he wished to settle his account in cash and handed over around £200 in bank notes. I didn't like to count it in front of him, preferring to trust that his pecuniary skills were better than his knowledge of the highway code.

When I arrived home and asked Judy to pay the money into the practice account, the bank politely told us the amount, although correct, was largely in expired £20 notes. Fortunately, the bank accepted the historical notes.

Sometimes, there was a contrast between patients. In one month quite soon after I had started in the practice, a young patient was very late for his appointment, keeping others waiting. Bypassing the receptionist, he strode into the surgery offering no apology and sat himself down. "You're very late," I said. "I have another patient due so I will see you afterwards."

"You won't," he said. "You will see me now. My time is more important." He found out it wasn't.

That same week, a wealthy patient well known for his sporting connections and philanthropy, came for a routine appointment. Clearly, sport was a topic of conversation, but I had to limit my contribution to tennis which was a sport I knew a little about and was particularly interested in.

It was Wimbledon fortnight and he asked if I was going to the tournament. Sadly, I told him that I had been unsuccessful in the ballot. At the end of the appointment, he left the surgery, and I could see him loitering outside the door on his mobile phone. He came back in a few minutes later. "Would you like two tickets for Wimbledon on Thursday? I have two debenture seats and you are very welcome to them." I jumped at the chance. These unexpected acts of kindness made a big impression.

And so, on that final day in May 2018, with Judy, I loaded all my possessions into the car and we left Harley Street for the last time. This was a sad, emotional farewell. Leaving many years of practice behind me, a life I had so enjoyed. As we drove through the West End and down to

Kensington, across the Thames over Hammersmith Bridge, my mobile rang. On the screen flashed up the caller's name: 'Mrs Buzzy'. My heart sank. "Dr Feaver," she said, "it's 'Mrs Buzzy' here. I just wanted to wish you a Happy Retirement!"

AFTERWORD

Retirement opened up new horizons. Abi and David, who had married two years earlier, had a baby boy, Finn. The arrival of our first grandchild brought new joy into our lives. There was sadness, too. My mother passed away the following year, aged 106. She had been born into an era with no wireless and no telephones and had lived through two world wars and survived the Spanish flu pandemic of 1919.

Just as I was adapting to life without patients, the world was plunged into crisis with the arrival of a new pandemic, COVID-19, and life changed for everyone. New words entered our vocabulary: lockdown, social distancing, track and trace, and many others. Everyone understood PPE, a term previously used only by clinicians. Whilst the NHS and care workers fought valiantly to treat and look after those afflicted by COVID-19, other front-line workers delivered essential services.

I have written in these pages of the heroism displayed by a previous generation in the Second World War. Suddenly finding ourselves in the midst of a devastating COVID pandemic, the country was witness to another generation's heroic deeds and selflessness beyond measure in battles fought on a very different front line. There were no air raid sirens warning of impending destruction, just the incessant sirens of ambulances carrying the seriously ill to hospital and thousands of volunteers enlisting to help.

Elective treatments were put on hold as we slowly adapted to a new way of living. Dentists couldn't practise because of the risks of transmission of this new virus and where urgent dental treatment was provided, it had to be in special centres where full PPE was available. Some patients resorted to do-it-yourself dentistry. Meanwhile, some dentists volunteered to join doctors and nurses caring for patients on the COVID wards.

At the height of the pandemic in 2020, Clare and Chris had a little girl, Phoebe. A lockdown baby and, like many others born in the midst of this coronavirus pandemic, her birth brought new hope for future generations. This was echoed at the peak of the second wave of COVID-19 the following year, when Abi and David had a baby girl, Mia, bringing joy to the dark days and a symbol of optimism for the better times to come.

PUBLISHED SOURCES

James Holland. *Fortress Malta. An Island Under Siege 1940–1943*. Phoenix 2004.

Maziar Bahari. *Then They Came for Me*. Oneworld 2012.

ACKNOWLEDGEMENTS

I want to thank all those patients who, over the years, put their trust in me and shared their stories, made me laugh and cry, and confided in me. I am indebted to the many colleagues who have helped me, some of whom I have already mentioned in these pages. Particular thanks go to Martin Gealer, whom I first taught when he was a student at Guy's. We continued to meet regularly throughout my years of practice to discuss opinions and advice on treatments for our patients. An invaluable exchange of ideas, especially when working in single-handed practice. Thanks as well to Michael Szasz, whom I met on my first day at Guy's and who has been a good friend and colleague since, often a source of wise counsel and always willing to provide cover for my patients when needed. I am also grateful to George Remington, friend and physician, a colleague for nearly forty years, twenty of which were at Marks & Spencer.

I am grateful to the nurses who worked with me in practice over the years and to the technicians who supported me.

To protect the privacy of some of those in my stories, I have altered their names or personal details. To those, and also to those I haven't mentioned by name, I am grateful for adding to the rich diversity, warmth and humour that I have encountered over the years. I hope that I have not offended anyone; if I have, I am truly sorry.

I am also grateful to Lesley de Gray for sharing with me the story of her father, Herbert Grunwald, and his escape from the tyranny of Nazi Germany.

My thanks to Peter James for his kind words and my thanks to Caroline Blackadder, a friend for over forty years, for her valuable comments and also to the wider family for their encouragement. A special thank you to Katy MacLeod as the first to read my book and to my brother-in-law David MacLeod for his guidance.

My son-in-law, David, eased my path to retirement by generously giving me the guidance and help I needed when selling my practice.

Above all my thanks to Judy for her love and support. She was the voice of reason and the inspiration that made my career possible, and to Clare and Abi for their love and encouragement and for making me laugh.

ABOUT THE AUTHOR

After qualifying as a dentist at Guy's Hospital in 1976, Gerald Feaver enjoyed a number of roles in hospital, teaching and general practice, retiring in 2018.

During his career, he lectured widely abroad and in the UK, helping to raise awareness of oral cancer. He is a Fellow of the Royal Society of Medicine and a past president of the dental section.

He is married with two daughters and lives with his wife in South-West London, close to his expanding family.

For exclusive discounts on Matador titles,
sign up to our occasional newsletter at
troubador.co.uk/bookshop